RED

THE WATERSTONES ANTHOLOGY

Waterstones

Published by Waterstones Booksellers Ltd.

First published in Great Britain in 2012 by Waterstones Booksellers Ltd.

www.waterstones.com

A CIP catalogue record for this book is available from the British Library.

Produced by Riot Communications/The Curved House.
Designed by Emma King.
Printed and bound in Great Britain.

ISBN 978-1-902603-74-2

Contents

FOREWORD

James Daunt

We have no lack of wonderful books to recommend to you. The frustration of a bookseller, if any, is to think of the great titles you are not advocating even as you champion something wonderful. So why, then, for the first time in many years, is Waterstones itself adding to the mix?

The answer, quite simply, is for the fun of it. *Red* assembles a great collection of writing – short fiction, polemic and poetry – by some of the best writers of the day. It has been a privilege to assemble and we hope gives great pleasure to everyone who reads it.

INTRODUCTION

Cathy Galvin – Editor

The best writing signals danger and passion. Bold and beautiful, it represents all the naked openness of the heart. It evokes joy and remembrance. It stops us in our tracks. It can be startling, sexy, revolutionary – the colour of blood. It is *Red*.

Our world changed in 2012. This anthology offers us glimpses into the past and future in newly commissioned work from some of the leading fiction writers, essayists and poets published in Britain. This year we have shared sporting and cultural highs; suffered political and economic lows. We have felt happiness, pride and fear. These pages capture the mood of an extraordinary moment in time.

Using a palette that explores the changing hues of intimacy, loss and wonder, our writers have created multiple shades of red, registering the shifts in our history and our sense of who we are in the world – ranging from the deepest crimson of the legacy of terrorism in Hanif Kureishi's short story to the cherry-red erotic discovery of Christopher Reid's poetry. From the *cri de coeur* of Will Self's polemic on the failure of the literary elite to Max Hastings' poppy-red lament for our armed forces.

Anthony Horowitz plunges into a tale infused with the blush-red of humiliation; John Gray strikes an academic's red pen across the map of Europe. The scarlet of love and its failures is played with in an unsettling memoir by Rachel Cusk, while its triumphs are explored in fine short stories by Emma Donoghue, Cecelia Ahern and Victoria Hislop. Poet David Harsent shoots to kill and fellow poet Alice Oswald offers up the glory of blood. The quiet red mist of female anger is dissected by Lionel Shriver in her story about the value of the dead and Suzanne Moore simply sees red in her attack on the decline of feminism. Andrew Motion and David Almond set the rose-tinted spectacles of childhood memory to one side: the first in reflections on a remembered landscape; the second in a magical tale of post-apocalyptic survival. Jackie Kay's poignant story shows us the beauty of commitment to a cause and a marriage. Simon Van Booy offers an everyday fairytale sprinkled with seasonal magic.

Red seeps through these pages like a fine wine, warm and occasionally intoxicating. Time to raise a glass to ourselves, to new beginnings, to writers and the people they write for.

CATHY GALVIN IS A JOURNALIST AND FOUNDER OF THE STORY SALON.

THIS DOOR IS SHUT

Hanif Kureishi

More or less the last thing Farhana remembered before finding herself on the Boulevard Saint Germain was her son Yasin waking up his driver and her guard and ordering them to take her to Karachi airport. As Yasin was too drunk to drive her himself, he instructed the men to put Farhana on the 2 a.m. flight to Istanbul, where she could change for Paris.

Yasin, who had not long before dragged her across the marble floor by her loveliest silk chiffon dupatta, and struck her across the face with the back of his hand, smashing her lip, now bowed before his mother. He said that after her behaviour she should never come back to Pakistan. And since he doubted whether he would live to be old, or that he would go to the West again, it was, as he put it, goodbye, or "*Khuda hafiz.*"

"May Allah protect you, and, never forget this −" his mother said, wagging her finger at him as she was helped into the car, "Allah is always watching you."

She could hear him laughing as she closed the window.

The following morning, once more wrapped in her favourite trench coat, she was walking around her adopted city. First she'd

1

go to the market; then, perhaps, she'd go to an exhibition, or look again at *la hune* her favourite bookshop, or the other wonderful little places on the Left Bank where she lived, selling hand-made paper and bizarre knick-knacks. In the afternoon she liked to go to the Tuileries or the Luxembourg for a sorbet, watching the children with their au pairs. There was plenty to see. When her first husband had been alive, she'd been a photographer, selling her pictures to Pakistani papers and magazines, and she knew how to look. It wasn't that Paris looked different now; she had only been in Karachi for a month. But she was full of new words, and would talk about the city differently, when she had the opportunity.

Farhana's husband Michel, a retired critic and journalist, was, as always at that time of the morning, reading in his study on what she called his *charpoy* – his day-bed – supported by oriental tasselled cushions. He hadn't seen his wife the previous night, and now he didn't get up to greet or kiss her, as if it would take too much physical effort. He didn't say he was glad to have her home. But he did wave, lean forward a little, and say, "You *are* back early. What happened to your lip?"

"I'll tell you, darling," she said. "I'll tell you everything."

He did say he was keen to hear her story. Not that she knew how to tell it. It would have to come out as it came.

In the late 90s, Farhana's first husband, an army general who had been educated in America, had been publicly beheaded by the Taliban at the behest of his army colleagues who thought he had become too pro-American. They believed, in fact, that he was betraying the complicity of the army with the Taliban to their mutual enemy the Americans. For this reason he was captured and driven to the mountains. After she had been sent a photograph of a hand holding up his head, with a large crowd of cheering local villagers in the background, she had fled. Yasin had refused to join her, but remained on the family's country estate, keeping out of politics.

Farhana went to Paris to stay with a wealthy friend who advised her never to go home. It would also be a good idea to find a steady man to look after her. Paris was ideal for exiles; once, it had welcomed the stateless. But Farhana would have little money and no status, and the French were notoriously racist, only liking people of colour if they were artists or could play the trumpet. What if they mistook her for an Algerian?

Farhana didn't seem concerned, and went along with others' wishes as if she only wanted a quiet life. Now, looking back, she guessed she was traumatised, and probably still was.

The good friend did a good thing and found the widower Michel, who was ten years older than her. Now in his mid seventies, he had retired from regular writing in order to read Balzac, study Trollope in English, and become properly familiar with the history of poetry. He had stuck to his word: he was a reader. His chosen destiny made him happy.

At the time he was seen as a tremendous catch, an opportunity not to be missed. He was widowed, well-off, cultured, well-connected, with numerous books to his name and a lovely flat off the Rue du Bac, on the Left Bank, full of pictures and theatre memorabilia. Farhana, a woman who had never before had to tell anyone who she was, was informed often that she was lucky. More than a thousand Parisian women would have wanted this dry old stick. But it was she, a frightened declining Pakistani woman then in her mid fifties, who had grabbed the prize. How? She guessed that because she said so little to him, she seemed more demure and mysterious than the others. She certainly had had no idea what she was doing. Perhaps he had pitied her.

It was indeed the case that Michel knew actors, writers and directors. Many of them were distinguished or even world famous in their own world, and they came for dinner once a month and drank a lot. The talk was always of the latest films and books, of what Sarkozy was, or wasn't, doing. If Farhana wondered what Michel wanted from her, there really was no obscurity. They had never been moved by one another. It was companionship: he liked someone to be there while he talked – an urgent and more or less continuous monologue concerning what was in the newspapers. He liked having someone arrange the film screenings he went to, and the plays he attended, often with her. He liked her to sit with him when he listened to the whole of symphonies by Brahms or Beethoven, nodding at her instructively during the finer parts. She loved this, as it was an opportunity for her to think about important things, and missed opportunities.

The friend who arranged the marriage included a warning. "Until the age of sixty a woman still needs passion. But I suspect, dear girl, that your man will make love like a critic."

"Without asking for it, one day I ran to the airport and found myself dumped in a completely new life, as a middle-aged immigrant," said Farhana. "How would I know how a critic makes love?"

"Watch out," said her friend. "*Fastidious*."

Farhana and Michel had sex twice: once before the marriage, and once after, which was more than enough for him. The first time he ejaculated immediately, and the second he suffered cramp and howled awfully, followed by a coughing fit which he had thought was a heart attack. Farhana suspected the catastrophe might have been caused by her removing his tie. She had never seen him during the day without a tie, and she only saw him at night, wrapped in a dressing gown, if they both had insomnia. She had bought him a cashmere polo-neck one Christmas, but Michel felt his being was an obscenity without a tie, and he never wore casual clothes.

Farhana thought she was done with her homeland; she had been ripped from the past, and the future was comfortable but null. Then, one afternoon, Yasin's wife Nasira, who had escaped him at last to London, insisted on coming to Paris to talk. Now working for a travel agent in Cricklewood, north London, Nasira came from a famous family, and had been a Cleopatra, one of the most striking women of Karachi, who wore the most glamorous saris and shimmering *shalwar kameez*, with solid gold bangles. Many men had been wild about her, which was, Yasin insisted, part of the problem. Now, in jeans and a sweater, she was – apart from the Rolex – as diminished and plain as Farhana realised that she herself was. But these two women, both escapees, liked one another and had much in common.

Farhana put her fingers under Nasira's chin and raised her face. "Why have you come to see me here?"

"I must warn you," Nasira said. Farhana's wild-tempered son, never the most stable of people, was developing into a madman. Out on his country estate in Sind, where he was a feudal landlord, Yasin was, apparently, playing polo aggressively, drinking whisky, copulating brutally, and shooting his many guns at anything alive around him. And because of the kidnappings, he was trying to import a brand-new armoured BMW with blacked-out windows into the country. His wife believed that, although this tank was extremely heavy and therefore somewhat slow, the "local Mr Toad", as she called her husband, would smoke a joint, turn up his favourite Punjabi bhangra music, and soon embrace a tree with the vehicle. Although she despised him, she didn't think another violent death in the family would be good for Farhana.

"What can I do about it?" Farhana asked. "Are you saying I must go there? I'm too weak now: I can't face it."

"You can only feel you have done your duty," her daughter-in-law replied. "And then live your life – which is what I am doing at last."

Haltingly, Farhana asked Michel if he would be interested in accompanying her, but he asked if it would be dusty, or inconvenient for his stomach. That was the least of it. Still, she made sure to take her first husband's gold watch, cuff links and fountain pens, which she would deliver to Yasin at last.

On her first afternoon in Paris after the trip, her husband asked her to walk with him. Today there was a wind, and he had his waistcoat on. As always, his hands were behind his back. Leaning forward, he barely lifted his feet from the ground, for fear of falling. "An old man can come to believe that he could easily be knocked down," he said. "If he takes a step –"

Farhana interrupted to say, "When you return to a country after a terrible shock, and more than a decade away, you will know that the roads will have got wider and the skyscrapers higher. There will be more apartment blocks, more people on the street, new immigrants and tourists coming to see the sights. Michel, I must be ageing because I remember when Karachi was a pleasant post-colonial city."

"Tell me!"

"The men wore suits and the women dresses. People still read Somerset Maugham, drank gin-and-tonics, and listened to 'In the Mood', as if the British had just popped north for the summer. There were flowers in the centre of the road. You could get *The Times* at your club. This time I saw rubble everywhere, a gun every ten yards, high walls and barbed wire. The women outside were afraid and covered themselves to avoid harassment. A city in lock-down, a war zone after a war. A state of petrifaction. Decline and decay everywhere."

Yasin had returned from his estate to welcome his mother. During the brief period he was sober, after he woke up around lunchtime and his servant went in to cut his toenails and shave him, Farhana went to his room. Although he had put on weight, and his body was flabby, his head was also shaven now, making him look thuggish.

Visas to the West were almost impossible to obtain these days; terrorism had rendered Pakistanis pariahs. All the same, Farhana wanted to persuade Yasin, before he destroyed his health, to do his best to escape to the West or even, since times were hard, to Australia or New Zealand, if he could bear it.

He laughed and replied, "There is no doubt that we have made a mess of things here. We all love to declare our devotion to the country, but apart from Imran Khan, every single one of us, if offered a visa, would pack hurriedly and rush to the exit tomorrow. But, I am sorry, mother, I will not be joining the others at the border humbly begging to be let into the land of plenty and reason. Being 'tolerated' is the last thing I want, having a low 'toleration' level myself."

"Darling, please, give me one good reason for you not to start a new life."

"It is here that the reality of the world is lived out."

The last time he was in France, with his then wife, Yasin said he saw a sign saying "Disneyland Paris" and laughed so much he wished, for the only time, that his father was also around to appreciate it. He had come to dislike the West more as he grew older, and had developed a particular animus against the authority of the EU, which he seemed to believe was run by Dominique Strauss-Kahn. He said not only was the EU hypocritical, but Europe was "risk-free and easy". Everything was polite and over-careful in its "multiculturalism and love for homosexuals". The brutality was now exported, with only Muslims as victims now, whom the West had never given up believing were lesser beings.

He said, "Our family sacrificed good lives in India to ruin this new country. As you know, we are a wild and self-destructive people who live carelessly. Life is cheap, only alcohol is expensive. Think how direct we are: all the hotels have been attacked with suicide bombs. When I walk out onto the street I like to know what the chances are that I will be shot at. Which other country in the world would hide Osama Bin Laden in the centre of a city while pocketing vast amounts of American money to finance the search for him? Mother, you must agree it takes perverse genius of the highest order to walk through that looking glass."

"It's not comfortable to be so stressed."

"You stress us, with your drone bombings of civilians." He asked, "How is your husband, the man who replaced my father? Do you like him? I can see from your lack of expression that you really don't mind, but you did hurry into his arms very quickly."

"Forgive me, but I was half-dead and stunned. I'm diabetic, and was diagnosed with extreme anxiety. Day by day I sewed my life back together. Michel gets up in the morning with purpose. You lie there like a teenager."

"Even if that man's work is pointless?"

"He writes about plays."

"But what would *Hay Fever* mean here?"

"He respects himself. You say you are religious, but you wallow in cynicism. Didn't you say, in this country the educated have no religion, and the religious have no education?"

"I am not religious," he said. "But I am a Muslim."

"Yasin, it is this country which has corrupted your imagination. Your father wasn't like this. He kept saying that without many voices, including the Christian, devotion to one religion will make us autocrats."

"Then the fool was begging to be murdered. He would have handed over the country to Jews, colonialists and those who want to bomb us into fundamentalist capitalism. Who here doesn't think that Osama taught those arrogant imperialists a good lesson?" He laughed. "But are we really to discuss this, Gertrude, mother?"

"You are too old for Hamlet."

There were no theatres, bars or new restaurants in Karachi, and people went to one another's houses. At first she accompanied her son on his nightly round of parties. It was an opportunity for her to see the people she'd grown up with, and for them all to notice how much they had aged.

She kept thinking she had been too long in Paris, for the houses she visited looked dusty, run-down and out of date, as if they weren't worth the expense of renovation. Soon she realised that anyone with money, intelligence, education or talent had left, and that the rest were urging their children to escape. They sold their jewellery and ushered them towards the border, saying, "Get out and never return." Her friends' children had joined an international class of wealthy but dispossessed people with American accents who now lived in Beijing, Prague or Toronto, working in hospitals or for law-firms or banks. Those left behind were the aged, infirm and hopeless, or those with too many dependents.

At the parties there'd be small-talk followed by ferocious drinking. It had been a long time since she'd seen people so shamelessly drunk they were lying under tables. Among the drunkest would be Yasin, whom she'd help home at four in the morning. In order to let him into the house, he made the servants remain awake until his return. He would either fall asleep then, or demand a woman, and she found herself fighting with him over the age of the servant girls he took. Fourteen, she said, was too young. Soon she stopped accompanying him, and stayed in the house.

There was nothing to do. She began to sit at the ping-pong table in the living room and write about her life, sometimes by candlelight, since the electricity failed more than twice a day. At least the cook and the servant girl took her seriously, creeping in with big smiles, and kebabs, onion bhajis and mango lassi on a tray, while the sweepress with orange teeth, crouching unnoticed for hours, flicked at the dust across the room. In exchange, Farhana made sure to give them little gifts, shawls, underwear, sandals and loose change.

It was three weeks into the month-long visit that, one afternoon, as she wrote, Yasin came yelling into the room, waving his pistol and saying his father's legacy of watch, pens and cuff links had been stolen, and he was having the house searched.

"I expect you just threw it all in a drawer, Yasin. Look again."

"They are happening all the time, these thefts. The people are poorer than you can conceive, mother. But the cook is particularly naughty. My eye has been on him since I noticed he dyed his beard. He has been filling the fridge with meals no human being has the capacity to eat – I suspect he is feeling guilty. He is our George Clooney – the male king-pin – and the neighbourhood servant girls are in and out of the kitchen, a place I never enter, as you know. Being a kind man, I pay for the abortions on a 'three-strikes-and-you're-out' basis. After that, the girls are sent to their village where they are reviled, persecuted and sometimes killed for their shame. Since I'm not a hundred percent sure it is that exact bastard, I will follow the correct procedures …"

"Good, thank you. Now put the gun away, you're frightening me."

She was reassured, in a place where, increasingly, she realised no reassurance was possible. Her closest friend, an English teacher with whom she'd been at school, was kidnapped while driving to meet Farhana. Her car was sandwiched between two other cars until it could only come to a stop; her driver had been dragged out at gunpoint, beaten and thrown into a ditch. The woman was blindfolded and taken to a house which, when she could see, resembled a waiting room. At least twenty other kidnappees sat on the floor, waiting for their families to provide money, while other victims were brought in.

On the afternoon in Paris, as Farhana strolled with her husband, she continued to explain, "My friend has always taught English literature, but more recently wanted to add a post-colonial module so the students might glimpse themselves in an artist's words. But there was a void in the curriculum because she cannot teach Rushdie, or even mention his name. She went into a shop to buy *Midnight's Children*, and the owner shouted, 'Get out – how dare you mention these hush-hush matters! You can look at pictures of men having sex with camels, or with children or babies. You can call for the death of the apostate. But promote that writer and this place will be ashes – Mullah Omar said this in 2005! Why can't you read P.G. Wodehouse like everyone else!'"

Farhana's husband, when he heard this, said, "I am reminded that I saw Milan Kundera the other morning, across the street. He walks to his office every day at the same time. I stop and bow respectfully as he passes. Of course he pretends not to notice me."

"He doesn't notice you," she giggled. "Why should he notice every old man who stops on the street and then genuflects like a madman?"

"I know he notices me. As I say, he prefers not to look up since he is thinking creatively." He went on, "At the beginning of *The Book of Laughter and Forgetting*, if I remember correctly, a Czech politician, Clementis, soon to be accused of treason and hanged, is erased from a photograph, leaving only the hat he passed to Gottwald on the day. They are doing the same in your country."

"They despair, and cling to the old certainties because they think the writer tears them apart."

"Though it is unbearable, they should be grateful, since he has done them the favour of speaking their disloyalty. The artist chews and digests the world for us, and then presents us with evidence of our humanity. What stands between us and barbarism?"

"Your tie."

"Apart from my tie, Farhana, there is the complexity of literature. If they cannot see that, they are lacking in the civilisation you see around you. Anyone here could tell you that extreme religion can only create sacrilege and perversion – like Catholic France producing the Marquis de Sade."

"Please, you go too far, Michel."

"But how is the boy?"

"The conditions in which he lives have put a jinn inside him."

"What a massive human effort it must have been to make such a wasteland!"

"And you cannot go onto the street without seeing people carrying rifles and machine guns. When I look around here – at this city – at the people walking peacefully, and the hundreds of years of accumulated achievement, I wonder how it's done."

"Thank God you have seen that, Farhana. I never thought you noticed where you were. What you describe is not achieved by driving out the Jews, Hindus, Catholics, and anyone who adds to the character and creativity of a city, until you have a monotonous monoculturalism – a new puritanism. If you let the pleasure-haters do that, there will be nothing living." He stood and looked around at the city as if he had built it himself. "The careful preservation of the past is the basis of culture. After the Second World War we learned how destructiveness stalks us, and how fragile civil society is."

She said, "Everywhere around the world the young are rising up, but in Pakistan they are going to the airport. I've never before been to a place without hope, nor anywhere without one beautiful thing in it, apart from the orchids in my son's garden."

Michel said, "This door – to the West – is shut now. In here it is an exclusive spa. Farhana, we are glad to have you, provided you respect our liberality."

"I do!"

"Count yourself lucky to have slipped inside."

"Thank you for reminding me, husband."

"Now tell me, how is it you made such a boy?"

"I will think about that – in my writing."

"Writing, did you say? Farhana – no!"

Yasin had had the house searched several times. "It's gone," he said at last. "We can't find any of it. The only things father left me. I want you to know, mother, that I let my servants eat meat, which is like caviar to them. I give them food which is not rotten. And of course they steal from me, and only rarely, when I am really wild, do I whip them. They would never be treated so well elsewhere, and this is how they reward me."

"It is mislaid, please, believe me," she said. "I have come here and seen that you are a victim awaiting a murderer. Please look more – behind the sofa, for instance – before you follow the procedures."

In Karachi she began to call it work now, her writing. Hadn't her life been more interesting than most? An arresting opening had occurred to her: she would begin with her two husbands, and compare Parisian men, their world and methods of love, to those of the men of Pakistan.

She began to get down to it as soon as she woke up, hunched over the ping-pong table, with some rotis on a plate and two standing fans turned on full. It was the only time Farhana felt content and safe in the country, and she had begun this work away from Paris since she knew that, far from encouraging her, Michel would condemn her work as "a waste of effort". It was his job to condemn the bad stuff. "Even before it is written?" she said when discussing the idea with him. "That *would* be confinement – and premature."

Now she said to Michel, "I feel as if I have had two men, you and my son, chattering and bullying me in the ear."

"Bullying?"

"Don't you see you are beginning to operate more like a big fat censor than a critic. I will resist you," she said. "I will even mention to your friends and perhaps to the concierge that I am writing! How the filthy foreign woman stains the *quartier* with her amateur words!"

"Please. Not that."

"If you don't announce it to them next time at dinner, there will be a fuss. Look at my cut lip – there is evidence."

She saw, when she told Michel this, that he was afraid; she might stand up to him and, in time, gain an advantage.

On her last evening in Karachi she returned from a visit to her friend to find the gates locked. The guard, who sat on a chair outside with his rifle, didn't come to her car. Instead her driver had to get out of their vehicle to let her into the house. Inside, it was silent, and it was never silent: there were more staff than family.

She called her son. "Where is everyone?"

"I've had enough. I'm following the procedures."

"What procedures?"

"I set a deadline for the return of my possessions but they were not recovered. I ordered the police to take everyone away. You will see how soon, *inshallah,* my belongings will come back."

"How?"

"It is tragic, mother, but you and I will have to get our own food tonight. The servants are hanging upside down on meat hooks in the police station. They will be there for a few hours, in their own urine and faeces, until they begin to feel uncomfortable. Meanwhile, I am waiting for the Security Expert to become available."

"Security expert? What is that?"

"The torturer. This service has now been privatised. We are following your example in the West. He is available by the hour, and I will tip him if the result is positive. What is a fingernail here or there? This is not *Downton Abbey.* Let's say it is more like your Guantanamo."

"No, Yasin."

"Mother, you will see how efficiently we can do things, after your determination to find nothing good in this ravishing country."

The bell rang. Before she went to her room to think, Farhana saw Yasin and the torturer taking whisky in the living room. She pictured the servants, with whom she'd been friendly – asking for their stories – in the police station.

When she heard the car start in the yard, and the two men got up and went outside, blood and fury rose to her head, and she went to her son before he drove away.

"I am outraged by this. You must not do it. I forbid it absolutely."

"You don't live here."

"I said I forbid it."

"Excuse me."

"I do not excuse you. He can tear my body instead." She turned to the torturer. "Open your bag and start on me! Tear out my heart, bastard! It was me who stole the things! Okay! I don't care if I live or die!" She began to expose her upper body. "Begin here!"

"You're making a fool of yourself, mother. Leave the man alone. I have paid him and can't afford to waste money."

"I attacked Yasin then," she said to Michel. "I went for his eyes with my nails, I was so outraged by what he had become. Then I ran into my room, took the sheet from the bed, tied one end around my neck and threw the other over the propellers of the fan. I was beginning to die when they came in. They released me and pulled me down, chased me, and Yasin pulled me across the floor. I was screaming so much, it was a nightmare for them. He struck me, but still I insisted he bring the servants back."

"And did they?" asked Michel.

"Later I saw them come in, a bedraggled bunch, the women weeping as Yasin got me into the car and sent me away."

"You did a good thing, my dear."

She took his arm. Her husband, walking beside her, looked at the lighted cafés, the churches and the shops, and hummed a song.

She said, "I want to believe that people can make good lives and can even be happy, despite what has happened to them and the burdens they have to bear."

"Yes," he said. "It would be a good idea to believe that."

HANIF KUREISHI IS THE AUTHOR OF NUMEROUS NOVELS, SHORT STORY COLLECTIONS, SCREENPLAYS AND PLAYS. HE HAS BEEN AWARDED THE CHEVALIER DE L'ORDRE DES ARTS ET DES LETTRES AND A CBE FOR SERVICES TO LITERATURE. IN 2008 *THE TIMES* LISTED HIM AS ONE OF 'THE 50 GREATEST BRITISH WRITERS SINCE 1945' AND IN 2010 HE WAS AWARDED THE PEN PINTER PRIZE.

THE CAT THIEF

Rachel Cusk

I met Amanda when she rang at the door one evening to ask if we had seen her kitten. Cats were always going missing in our street. What could the reason be? The lamp posts were covered in forlorn notices, wrapped in plastic to protect them from the rain: *Has anyone seen Domino, Midnight, Tom?* As well as breed, colour and distinguishing marks, the owners frequently described temperament, something I myself would find hard to ascertain in a cat. To say a cat is playful, adventurous or shy is to be able to see through its self-satisfaction; I find the approval-seeking dog, with its capacity for shame, far less alien.

Often there were photographs of the missing cats, wide-eyed in the camera's flash, and the dates of disappearance, melancholy as a child's tombstone. Yet such things could have meant little to the average passerby. It was as though their owners needed a public commemoration of their loss. In the photographs the cats were usually shown reclining amongst cushions, surrounded by the kinds of rattles and playthings you might give a baby. That someone should go to so much trouble over an animal then to lose it is mysterious in itself. Occasionally I wondered whether people who had a more cavalier or even neglectful attitude to their cats were more likely to hang on to them, and if so what this said about the cat character; but the real enigma was the sheer frequency with which these disappearances happened in the street where I live.

Amanda knew nothing of all this: she had just moved down from London with her husband and two children.

"Look, I'm really sorry to bother you," she said, smiling brilliantly when I opened the door. "But the bloody cat has run away."

Only a week or two earlier, a girl had rung on the bell late at night, sobbing so disconsolately she could barely speak to say what was wrong. I could make out the word "Snowflake"; eventually she pulled herself together and between harrowing breaths said that Snowflake, a long-haired white Persian barely a month old, had completely vanished. They had put her out in the garden – "just for a minute!" the girl cried, agonised – but when they came to look for her she wasn't there. They were searching all the adjoining gardens on this side of the street: would I mind if she looked in mine? I showed her through and switched on the outside lights. For ten minutes or more she called and whistled and searched among the shrubs. Snowflake was not in my garden. Back on the doorstep, the girl began to cry again. "I can't bear to think what she's going through," she sobbed. "She's so tiny and young, and it's so dark, and she's all alone – and she probably can't find her way home!"

When you don't live in a big city you come to notice things about people who do. City-dwellers have an air of energy, of lusty curiosity, that might almost be called appetite: standing on my doorstep, Amanda looked me up and down with the assessing, almost devouring glint of someone measuring things up, figuratively speaking, for their next meal. In one hand she held her phone, and throughout our conversation the fingers of the other didn't pause as they moved speedily around the blue-lit screen. Yet her friendly, voracious gaze never seemed to falter. It was like being held in the beam of a spotlight while all sorts of activity went on backstage, in the darkness of the wings.

"It's just a tabby thing," she said cheerfully. "The children are devastated, of course. We've only had the little bastard for a fortnight."

I expressed sympathy and the beam intensified.

"Oh, you're a *darling*. I suppose he'll turn up eventually, when he's hungry." Her eyes wandered irresistibly over my shoulder. "I love what you've done with your hall," she said. "Are those the original floorboards?"

I didn't like to warn Amanda that she might not see her kitten again. Having only just arrived, it would upset her: she could have seen it as an omen, and perhaps it was, for I myself had lost things here. She seemed like a nice woman – part of me wanted to tell her to pack her bags and go back to town as fast as she could. But I said I would keep an eye out.

"Thank you *so* much darling," she said, touching my arm. "Listen, you must come round for a chat. I'm just up there, at number thirty-six. Drop by any time."

Later that night I was startled by the sound of scratching at the window that faced the street, and then by an enormous pair of pale-green eyes that stared frenziedly through the glass at me when I drew back the curtain. It was a tabby kitten, skinnily hunched on the window ledge. I opened the window and grabbed its soft light body, and it responded by sinking its tiny claws painfully into the flesh of my arm. Though it was late the lights were still on in Amanda's house. A man answered the door.

"I think this might be your cat," I said.

He was somewhat cat-like himself: for a long time he looked at me expressionlessly, and then his large eyes slowly blinked.

"That's very kind," he said softly.

He took the kitten and closed the door. But a few nights later the creature was on my window ledge again. This time, when I took it back, Amanda answered.

"Oh God," she said, "I'm *so* sorry. Come in and have a drink – have you got time? Tilly!" she yelled up the stairs as we passed into the kitchen. "Tilly, the bloody cat's back!"

I could hear a television on somewhere, the sound of gunfire and small explosions.

"That's the third time this week," Amanda said. She sloshed wine to the brims of two glasses. "Saul wants me to get rid of him."

"Is that your husband?"

"He's a bolter," she said, referring, I supposed, to the cat. "But it's meant I've met all the neighbours – isn't it incredible how many fascinating people live here?"

The truth was I didn't really know anyone in my street, unless you counted the boy whose music came through my bedroom wall all night, and who I was occasionally driven to remonstrate with through his intercom at three o'clock in the morning.

"Saul can't stand that, you see," Amanda said confidentially. "He can't bear people coming round. He says he doesn't want to know anyone here." She gave a snorting laugh. "He'd rather be in a bar in Soho."

"I think I met him," I said.

"Oh I'm sure he was charm itself to *you*. He loves women, and of course they all *adore* him."

I didn't contradict her, on either count.

She began rapidly to ask me questions: how I lived and with whom; what I did, who I knew, where I had come from, and how long ago. Amanda was evidently a woman of high social activity: her phone was a buzzing hive of calls and messages flying in and out, which she attended to without ever stopping what she was doing, so that she seemed to be living in two different dimensions at once. Her fingers were forever speeding across the blue-lit screen, and at several points our conversation involved a third party, squeaking *a capella* through the receiver that she held clamped between her jawbone and her ear while she waltzed among the kitchen units in clouds of steam cooking supper for her children. There was something comforting in the hectic atmosphere Amanda generated. It was like the heat from a fire: you couldn't help but draw closer.

A little girl had come into the room and was fondling the kitten, her nose pressed into its fur.

"Bad Red," she said. "Naughty Red."

"Why's he called Red?" I asked.

She lifted her eyes to my face and gave me the same long expressionless gaze I had received from her father.

"Red for danger," she said.

"Oh," I said. One reason I mistrust cats is for their air of enigma, which I've always suspected to be a foil for the most calculating self-interest. After all, a mystery is just a truth someone is concealing for reasons of their own. But the mystery of the missing cats had made me think again. It suggested the operation of some larger force, something dark and impersonal that had fastened on our street, something mindlessly bent on taking away what was loved. And a cat, though careful and selfish on its own account, can't help being loved.

A few weeks later I caught sight of Amanda, pacing up and down on the pavement outside my house. She looked agitated. Though the day was overcast she wore sunglasses, and her hair was yanked back into a matted ponytail. I opened the door to invite her in: she was, of course, on her phone, but she gave me a valiant little wave and held up five fingers, nodding and smiling and grimacing at whatever conversation she was having.

"It's all a bloody nightmare," she said, removing her sunglasses in my kitchen to reveal reddened eyes in deep violet pockets of shadow. "I've told Saul I'm chucking him out. I've had enough. He's got to go. Even the children agree."

"Don't," I said, before I could help myself. In that instant I had a vision, a vision of Amanda and her children standing as though on a precipice, or at the very top of a wild fairground ride. I saw it clearly, the long fall, reality left behind for the terrifying, inescapable loops and plunges of the Big Dipper, the whirling and spinning, the cataclysmic descents, and the three of them clinging on with their hearts in their mouths, their hearts forever in their mouths – even after all this time, mine was there still. "Please don't," I said.

Bleary eyed though she was, Amanda still managed to look astonished. "Darling," she said. "Are you all right?"

I didn't see much of her over the next month, though I saw a lot of Red. He was by now a certified pest, a marauder, forever hunting in my flower beds, catching birds, strutting shamelessly along the garden wall with his tail in the air. I had stopped taking him home: it was clear he could look after himself. Sometimes, passing Amanda's house, I detected signs of turbulence – the curtains drawn in the middle of the afternoon, the front door standing open, loud voices drifting out into the street – but then one afternoon she sent me a text: *Glass of wine 7ish this evening? Dying to catch up – it's been ages!*

Amanda's house was abuzz with activity. There was music playing in the kitchen and different music coming from upstairs, and the sound of television and doors banging and children's voices and some kind of hammering noise coming from the garden. A woman in a long vividly patterned dress sat at the table tapping something into her phone; a young Chinese boy stood before the open fridge, pondering its contents. Numerous saucepans bubbled on the stove and the sink was full of dirty dishes.

"Darling, how are *you*?" Amanda cried, above all the noise. "Sorry about all the mess."

She looked better, though thinner; the shadows had gone from beneath her eyes. She dashed around the kitchen getting glasses, stirring the saucepans, flinging more dirty plates into the sink.

The woman at the table introduced herself as Susie. She demurred when she was offered a glass of wine.

"Better not," she said. "I've got hot yoga later. If you drink they can smell it on your sweat. You've got the most intense yoga scene down here," she said, to me. "You're so lucky."

From the fridge the Chinese boy spoke unintelligibly.

"Susie's thinking of moving down from London, aren't you darling?" said Amanda.

"The other half's not so sure," Susie said. "But then again, I'm not so sure about the other half."

"What's that, Ang? Your noodles? They're just there at the back, behind the chicken. Found them?"

"Isn't she marvellous?" Susie said, to me. "She's got this place packed to the rafters with language students. Every door you open, there's another one."

"The bastard's refusing to pay a penny in maintenance," Amanda said cheerfully. "What else can I do? I'm going to have to rent out the children's bedrooms next."

Her phone rang and she answered it.

"No," she said after a pause. "No, I'm not bloody well going to do that."

Susie had risen from the table and was standing on one leg with the other twisted around it in an impossible-seeming contortion. Just then a man I didn't recognise came into the kitchen, followed by Amanda's small son. The man was very good-looking, in a well-fed, prosperous kind of way. Amanda held up her hand to him, mouthing and pointing at her phone. To my surprise he strode towards her, grabbing her around the waist and nuzzling her ear while she tried to continue her conversation.

"No. All right. No. No, don't. You know why not. OK, OK. Bye." She put down the phone, flustered. "Ben, lay off!" she said, turning her face away.

"We finished the tree house," he said, squeezing her harder while she tried in vain to push him off. Finally she relented and laughed.

"Did you? Is it good?"

"It's amazing," said the little boy. "Ben let me use the saw."

"Oh mate, don't tell her that," the man said, putting his hand comically to his forehead.

"Come and see," the boy said, tugging at Amanda's hand.

"That was Saul," Amanda said to Susie and me, rolling her eyes.

"Mum, Ben let me use the saw."

"You didn't, did you?" Amanda said to Ben. But her face was red with pleasure.

Susie had put on her coat, an extraordinary blanket-like garment that came to the floor.

"Must fly," she said. She kissed me on both cheeks. "Are you the writer? I'd love to be able to write – you're so lucky."

"Bye darling," Ben said.

Susie took him by his shoulders and fixed him with her eyes. "Take care of her," she said.

While Amanda was showing Susie out, Ben said to me:

"How do you know Amanda?"

I said I was just a neighbour.

"I'll be honest with you," he said, drawing close. "She's changed my life. I'm so happy I can't tell you."

"I'm glad," I said.

He looked at me consideringly.

"That's interesting," he said. "You look completely different when you smile."

"Ben's taking me to Paris tomorrow on the Eurostar," Amanda said, when Susie had gone and Ben had taken the boy back out to the garden. She blushed and put her hands to her cheeks. "I'm actually a bit nervous – isn't that ridiculous, at my age?"

The next day I got a text.

Darling, I'm worried about you. Have you thought about anti-depressants? Lots of my friends take them and absolutely swear by them – promise me you'll at least consider it! Amanda must have sent it just before the train went into the tunnel. I tried to imagine her there, under the English Channel, all contact for a while suspended, the blue screen quiet and null beneath the weight of water.

A few weeks later, cutting back the ivy that grows along the top of my garden wall, I happened to look across at the back window of one of the neighbouring houses. It is a large bay window: usually the ivy obscures this view, but now I could see straight into the ground-floor room. It was full of dark furniture, mahogany tables and sofas upholstered in rich-coloured cloth, lamps and a great leather-topped desk in the bay; and everywhere, stretched out on the table-tops or curled amidst the sofa cushions, sitting upright on the desk or lying sphinx-like along the windowsills in the sun, were cats, cats of every size and colour, and all as still as statues. I stood on my ladder and stared at the sight while at least forty pairs of eyes stared back at me unblinking. Then I climbed back down into my own garden.

RACHEL CUSK IS THE AUTHOR OF SEVERAL NOVELS AND THREE WORKS OF NON-FICTION, INCLUDING *A LIFE'S WORK: ON BECOMING A MOTHER* AND *AFTERMATH: ON MARRIAGE AND SEPARATION*. SHE IS READER IN CREATIVE WRITING AT KINGSTON UNIVERSITY.

TWO RED POEMS

Christopher Reid

THE CHERRY

Tell me, why should the first cherry,
the first cherry of summer,
always be the best?
Not the first bag,
though that may be good,
but the first piece of fruit.
Selected for its flawless shine,
tugged from its stalk,
introduced between tongue and palate
to be weighed there briefly,
assayed chiefly
for plumpness and firmness,
before committal to the teeth,
after less than a second
of poised, of proud, of poignant
refusal to betray its secret,
it succumbs to a single bite

that broaches the taut skin,
releasing a sharp-sweet spurt,
and mouth and cherry
rush to combine their juices
in a joyous union
that cannot be repeated
for four full seasons.
Why not? Finding out –
or, rather, attempting to –
accounts for many a belly-ache
and much heaviness of heart.
Forget reasons, just take
that first, ritual
taste-burst as it comes,
and, when you've sucked the stone clean,
leave the rest
of the bag you've just bought,
leave all the rest
of summer's seductive cherry crop,
well alone.

THE COCHINEAL

Now that the absolute
freshness of our brides
is less highly valued
than it was before,
the makers and merchants
of cochineal, that costly substance,
of which every fluid ounce
represents the gore
of a thousand crushed insects,
have been the first and loudest
to denounce and deplore
the moral laxness of our times.

CHRISTOPHER REID'S LATEST BOOK, *NONSENSE*, APPEARED FROM FABER & FABER IN SEPTEMBER. AMONG HIS RECENT VOLUMES, *A SCATTERING* WAS NAMED COSTA BOOK OF THE YEAR FOR 2009, WHILE *THE SONG OF LUNCH* BECAME A BBC2 FILM STARRING ALAN RICKMAN AND EMMA THOMPSON.

DEATH OF THE REDCOAT

Max Hastings

Thirty years ago, I found myself tramping across a soggy South Atlantic wilderness among 15,000 Royal Marines, paratroopers, Guardsmen and Gurkhas who were fighting that most surreal of campaigns, the 1982 Battle for the Falklands.

It was obvious at the time that Margaret Thatcher's South Atlantic adventure was a last imperial hurrah. But none of us would then have guessed that today, not merely the ships and planes, but the very armed forces which fought the war, would be on their way to the scrapyard. Soldiers are being made redundant. I do not mean merely those thousands of men and women who have lately been handed P45s as part of the coalition government's defence cuts. The entire British Army, as an institution, is shrinking towards a point where, like Alice's cat, soon only the smile will be left. This represents a big cultural change for Britain; but despite all the enthusiasm for supporting soldiers through such charities as Help for Heroes, there is no sign that the public has noticed, or if they have, that they much care. Amid the disillusionment following perceived military failure in Iraq and Afghanistan, the British people have lost their old enthusiasm for our traditional role as a warrior nation.

David Cameron's coalition government has made a decision – rooted not in any rational assessment of security needs, but solely in its desperate need to save money – to cut the army to its lowest manpower strength for centuries: 82,000 men. When the current downsizing process is complete in 2015, the army will have shrunk by more than 20 percent. It will be capable of deploying only a single battlegroup of 7,000–8,000 men for sustained operations overseas. This is a tiny force. Compare it to the 35,000 troops deployed in Northern Ireland at the height of the Troubles in the 1970s, or the 30,000 British military personnel sent to the First Gulf War in 1991.

The message is plain: Britain has neither the means nor the will any longer to sustain a capability to commit large numbers of troops abroad, in support of what a government decides is the national interest. The historic vision of the trusty redcoat – in the line at Blenheim, Waterloo, Balaclava; defending Rorke's Drift for that peerless movie *Zulu*; fighting to victory in two world wars and countless colonial 'brushfire' campaigns – is to be laid to rest.

This momentous decision, with all that it means for our culture and heritage, has been a long time coming. Some pundits suggest that, leaving aside the need to cut costs, soldiers no longer have much relevance to Britain's modern security needs. What are soldiers *for*, in the twenty-first century?

This is a fair question, which deserves an answer. For thousands of years, nations required armies – mostly recruited for specific conflicts rather than maintained on a permanent basis – to defend their own territories and conquer those of others. The British took pride in their victories over the French in the Hundred Years' War, despite the fact these were achieved by men who behaved on the continent like extreme soccer hooligans. From the eighteenth century onwards, though we continued to fight the French, on the whole successfully, most of our military effort was deployed to secure our burgeoning empire.

The public in those days did not love its soldiers as it did its sailors. The military historian Correlli Barnett has written: 'the history of the British army is the history of an institution that the British have always been reluctant to accept that they needed'. Everybody knew that Britain recruited its warriors from the dross of society, men incapable of finding any other route to a living than to 'take the King's Shilling'. The army preserved some respectability, chiefly because the British aristocracy had a hereditary enthusiasm for fighting, and purchased commissions for its younger sons. The upper echelons of society thus led into battle 'the scum of the earth, enlisted for drink'. The lords and honourables often lacked education or intelligence and were quite unfit for their commands, as Wellington complained. But somehow the raw, brutal, bovine courage common to both the leaders and the led enabled the army to achieve some remarkable things in battle.

Even when the purchase of commissions was abolished towards the end of the nineteenth century, a tradition persisted that British officers were drawn from the social elite, and sustained their reputation for stupidity. At the beginning of the First World

War, thousands of officers were killed gratuitously, because the convention was deep-rooted that a proper leader must flaunt his lack of fear. Lt Col. Walter Loring of the Warwickshire Regiment, for instance, led his men up the Menin Road from Ypres to face the Germans in October 1914, mounted on an enormous white horse. He cursed when a bullet struck his heel, and after having the wound dressed insisted on remounting. His hapless horse was soon killed, and Loring took another, which also perished. The colonel himself was eventually killed on 24 October, hobbling among his men, urging them on with one foot in a carpet slipper. It was tremendously gallant, and terribly silly. Lt Col. 'H' Jones was killed doing much the same thing at Goose Green in May 1982; Mrs Thatcher insisted for political reasons that he should receive a Victoria Cross, against strong opposition from the chiefs of staff.

The colonel, you may remember, at a critical moment of the battle of Goose Green, abandoned his increasingly desperate efforts to control his battalion's attack in order to launch a one-man charge on the Argentine position, behaviour most professional soldiers thought recklessly irresponsible.

Many armies, and especially the British, would have fared better through the ages had they esteemed courage a little less, cunning a tad more.

One of the changes wrought by the 1914–18 conflict was that it made the nation familiar, at a terrible cost, with what soldiering meant: much of the eligible male population had been conscripted.

Beyond the horrors of fighting in the mud and blood of France and Flanders, a whole generation of young men learned the ways of the army, hitherto confined to a few hundred thousand volunteers. They knew how to bone boots and shine brasses, to lay their trousers beneath the mattress to keep their creases, and to snap a salute whenever an officer passed. For nearly all those who served and survived, their time as soldiers lasted only two or three years of a lifetime. Yet, to this day, almost every household in Britain cherishes photographs of granddad or great-granddad posing in his tunic and service cap. For all the ghastly experiences the First World War imposed, many men forever afterwards cherished the experience of comradeship, and valued their own small part in upholding Britain's warrior tradition.

Between the wars, the armed forces shrank dramatically, and were starved of resources. When 1939 came, Winston Churchill was only the foremost of those shocked by the low quality of generalship and, once again, millions of young men experienced military life and took back into their natural civilian world in 1945 memories and loyalties which persisted to their deaths.

The Cold War and residual empire commitments sustained a relatively large army of 750,000 men in the 1950s, but it was then decided that conscription was more trouble than it was worth: regulars spent most of their time training an endless stream of resentful young men, yearning to get on with their 'real' civilian lives. Few of the millions who peeled potatoes or blancoed belts and puttees for two years at Aldershot learned much that was useful.

The professional army of the 1960s and 1970s, volunteers to a man, was arguably the best the country has ever had – far more skilled and serious, and better commanded, than Britain's soldiers in the two world wars. But it continued to shrink in size. Regardless of the strength and supposed might of the Warsaw Pact's huge forces deployed behind the East German border, Britain and its allies could not or would not pay for armies seriously capable of resisting a Russian invasion. A new doctrine evolved: Rhine Army and the troops of the other North Atlantic Treaty Organisation (NATO) nations were expected only to act as 'a tripwire'; to hold up the communist hordes for long enough for diplomacy to stop the fighting – or for the Western powers to use nuclear weapons. NATO's Cold War deployment in Western Europe was literally incredible: a gesture army, no more capable of stopping a Warsaw Pact assault than a line of policemen with riot shields. But at least NATO, by deploying the soldiers of many nations as a 'thin red line' in Germany, made a political commitment that was serious; and in those days there was still a visceral cultural belief that nations ought to have armies, and put them in harm's way.

The end of the Cold War frightened British professional soldiers. They feared – with good reason – that the government would seize upon the opportunity to save money by cutting the armed forces. The Royal Navy felt especially vulnerable, and was warmly grateful to Argentina for invading the Falklands in 1982. The prestige of the armed forces soared after securing a handy victory over the Argentines: a short, sharp, decisive war enabled the British to show off their superiority over a third-class enemy. The Falklands war gave as big a boost to national morale as the 2012 London Olympics, but has proved a long-term strategic misfortune. It created a commitment in the South Atlantic no government recognised before it was fought. The islands are of negligible value – I am sceptical about the taxpayer ever seeing any oil riches – but it is politically unthinkable to abandon them. Defending the Falklands and its 3,000 inhabitants – many of them expatriate contract employees – has cost around £5 billion since 1982; this is a mere prestige issue, irrelevant to other British strategic interests.

Margaret Thatcher earned her reputation as a warrior prime minister in the Falklands; but after paying the bills for replacing ships and equipment lost in the conflict, she resumed her pursuit of a 'peace dividend' from the ending of the Cold War. Rhine Army's resources and training budgets were cut savagely. When the First Gulf War came, it proved necessary to cannibalise the British Army's entire armoured vehicle inventory in Germany to deploy a single weak division in the desert. As the twentieth century drew to a close, British generals became increasingly desperate to identify roles which could justify the preservation of their regiments. They hated the muddled, inconclusive commitment to peace-keeping in Bosnia. Douglas Hurd, as foreign secretary, once said to me: "I wish your military friends would make up their minds whether they want to be in Bosnia or out of it. At the moment, they seem schizophrenic about it." I said: "You know jolly well why they are wobbling; they hate the lack of clear objectives, but know that if their men were brought home to Salisbury Plain, the Treasury would make half of them redundant."

The army was deeply apprehensive about its future when Tony Blair became prime minister in 1997, but its fears proved quite unfounded: New Labour's prime minister put British troops in harm's way, in pursuit of his supposed 'moral foreign policy', more often than any modern national leader, including Thatcher. There was one important difficulty, however. While Blair was eager to use force to do good deeds in the world, he never wanted to pay the bills. In Iraq and later in Afghanistan, British forces found themselves attempting to achieve huge objectives with small numbers of men, and humiliatingly dependent on the Americans for equipment, including helicopters. I remember meeting General Sir Michael Jackson, then head of the army, after he returned from a Washington meeting to plan the 2003 Gulf War. I asked how much influence the British were exercising on American operations. Jackson heaved a sigh and said: "Mass matters, and we don't have it." In the Blair era, the British Army, by now shrunk to 100,000 men, again and again accepted tasks that were properly beyond its means. The generals' traditional 'can do' spirit contributed to serious, long-running embarrassments both in Basra and Helmand province. The British Army was trying to play out of its league – or rather, out of any military league the taxpayer was willing to fund. Defence, which before the First World War accounted for almost one-third of tax revenue, now received only 5 percent.

In the final twenty years of the last century, the Falklands, together with operations in the Balkans, briefly suggested that the armed forces were effective deliverers of policy. That moment is now past. The public embraces our soldiers – but as victim figures. They are regarded as much as lambs to the slaughter as was the Light Brigade at Balaclava. David Cameron's coalition government recognises only that it needs to save money. It is determined to fight no more foreign wars, once we escape from the disastrous and unsuccessful entanglement in Afghanistan. This hope or expectation is probably unrealistic because events have a way of taking charge. The irony has not gone unnoticed by soldiers that, within weeks of decreeing draconian defence cuts, David Cameron took the lead in insisting on a Western military commitment to depose President Gaddafi of Libya. He now seems equally eager to act against the Syrian regime.

Who knows where else he, or his successors, may discern a 'moral imperative'? Downing Street would say: "Ah, but we have identified new ways of leveraging force which do not involve soldiers. Air power, sea-launched cruise missiles and special forces can do the business, without having to commit thousands of troops." But soldiers' 'boots on the ground' offer a flexibility no technology can match. Again and again, at home and abroad, the army has provided a disciplined and available resource no other institution can match. In 2012, the government would have faced huge embarrassment had it not been able, at a month's notice, to deploy 3,000 soldiers for security at the London Olympics, after the contracted security firm fell down on its commitment. Yet, after 2015, there will be pitifully few of them, for Olympic security or anything else.

If our soldiers, sailors and airmen 'lacked mass' a decade ago, henceforward matters will be much worse: they are shrinking to a point at which there can no longer be any pretence that they are capable of independent action. The RAF is burdened with hundreds of unsuitable aircraft, notably the Typhoon designed for high-level interception of Russian bombers during the Cold War. The Royal Navy has committed a madness by insisting on building two huge super-carriers, which mean that it lacks cheap, nimble frigates to carry out – for instance – anti-piracy patrols in the Red Sea.

When the carriers are complete, a small force of American F-35 aircraft is being purchased, to fly off them. Yet almost every airman today recognises that we are approaching the end of the era of manned combat aircraft. Drones, as used for reconnaissance and targeted killing on the Afghan border, point to the future. In a rational world, the navy would instead be getting cheap, cheerful carriers. We should be investing big in the unmanned future of aviation, instead of buying more obsolescent fast jets. If we end up entangled in conflict with China, this is far more likely to take the form of cyberwarfare than Biggles stuff over the Pacific. The RAF should logically become a mere corps of the army, though politics being what it is, this is unlikely to happen. Headlines would scream: "Who will defend us in the next Battle of Britain?" Almost any government would flinch from that sort of press.

And as for the army? It will continue to contribute modest contingents to international peace-keeping forces. The Special Air Service, Special Boat Service and affiliated support units will never be short of work in the new world. Politicians revel in the popularity and prestige of Britain's special forces, and international terrorism is here to stay. The thousand-odd men and women who make up the elite units have forged a new sort of military legend, and nobody is likely to allow that to atrophy or go unused.

But it seems to me a characteristic irony of history that a decade ago the West focused its fears overwhelmingly on the peril posed by al-Qaeda. Yet today we see, and our leaders see, that the economic and financial crises pose a challenge to Western hegemony and stability vastly greater than anything Osama bin Laden ever dreamed of.

Our European partners, with the sole exception of France, have almost resigned from professing serious defence and security policies. Though they still belong to NATO, most of their armed forces possess slender and diminishing capabilities, for they find it hard to see who they might fight. Even the incomparably wealthy and powerful United States is being obliged to make major defence cuts to stem its budget deficit.

The reality bearing down upon every government is that soldiers are phenomenally expensive. It costs about $2 million a year to keep each American soldier on the ground in Afghanistan. Manpower costs now account for 40 percent of Britain's defence costs when training, pay, housing, benefits and pensions are considered. The capital cost of technology is high, but seems to deliver a bigger bang for your buck, to use the old Washington saying. Computers, drones, missiles do not incur huge downstream costs for medical bills. Human rights and health and safety legislation stop being a problem if you can get human beings off the set. But many seductive voices, including those of sailors and airmen, mutter in ministers' ears: "We had lots of boots on the ground in Basra and Helmand, and they do not seem to have done much for Britain's national interest."

Though the British Army's commanders plead to keep their numbers up, they sometimes overlook the embarrassing fact that ever-fewer young men want to be soldiers. Recruitment in Scottish regiments is so poor that they rely on Fijiians to make up their strength. The army's officer class is likely to change in character – and, frankly, to diminish in quality – following the government's moves to eliminate alleged 'perks' and cut pensions. It will no longer be possible in future for even a successful senior officer to sustain an upper middle-class lifestyle – this by decree of a Cabinet many of whose members have large private fortunes. The government is looking to private defence contractors to provide an increasing proportion of the support services necessary in war zones. It is unlikely – in the short term, at least – that a British government will hire mercenaries to do its fighting. But the army is being cut to levels at which, if it is required to participate in a major combat operation overseas, heaven knows why or where, drastic expedients will be necessary to provide the means. Once a modern army has shrunk to the size of Britain's today, it is almost impossible to imagine a scenario in which it expands again.

Defence policy should always be rational, so no sensible person will lament the end of Britain's redcoat tradition merely as a matter of sentiment. But I believe that, for practical security reasons, we shall live to regret the drastically shrunken size the armed forces will attain from 2015 onwards. In future, at vast expense, we shall retain a capacity to pulverise an identified foreign enemy with Trident nuclear missiles, though it is hard to conceive any credible scenario in which we would use them. We shall still have the SAS, capable of storming buildings and fighting terrorists. But we shall have lost an immense and important amount of capability and flexibility in between the two.

When millions of British people put on their Remembrance poppies in November 2012, they will be commemorating not only the dead of our past wars, but the passing into history of the armed forces which have done so much to define our national culture for centuries. For better or worse our politicians are consigning Britain's army, navy and air force to the margin of national experience.

MAX HASTINGS IS THE AUTHOR OF SOME TWENTY-THREE BOOKS, THE MOST RECENT *ALL HELL LET LOOSE: THE WORLD AT WAR 1939–45*. HIS NEW WORK, *CATASTROPHE: EUROPE GOES TO WAR 1914*, WILL BE PUBLISHED IN SEPTEMBER 2013.

FRANCESCA AND THE TIGER

David Almond

We took Francesca to the tiger on the morning of my sixteenth birthday. I rose early, when the last stars were still in the sky. I found Father in the scullery already brewing tea. I could see he hadn't slept. He was trembling. I helped him to sit down, and I found some biscuit, a handful of tomatoes, and we ate together.

"Do we have to do it?" I said to him.

He sighed.

"It is what must be done."

I poured water into his tea to cool it. He slurped it from a shallow bowl.

"You must gather some cherries later," he said. "And did you remember the potato trench?"

"I did it yesterday."

Tomato seeds dribbled down his chin.

"She is old!" he said.

There were glimmers of light above the city as I guided him through the garden to her little stable.

She didn't move.

"She is sleeping?" said Father. "Then wake her."

I knelt down in the dust beside her and ran my hand over her head, the smooth covering of hair, the perfectly shaped skull beneath. I breathed into her ear and her gorgeously lidded eyelids opened.

"Come on, love." I whispered.

Her legs immediately began to shift, her hooves to scrape the hard stone floor.

"Slowly," I whispered.

I helped her struggle to her feet. I held a pail of water and she drank. I put cabbage and dried grass into her nosebag and she ate. I fastened the halter, the bridle, the body straps to her. I lifted the shafts of the cart and attached them to her. She stood head downward, uncomplaining, patient as ever.

"Good girl," said Father to her.

"Good boy," he said to me.

I lidded the pail of water and put it in the cart.

I didn't load it up with vegetables today.

I took Father's arm and helped him climb up. He took the reins.

"Now lead us out," he said.

I led her to the garden gate, unlocked it, led us into the street, locked the gate again.

"I could walk beside her today," I said. "It would be easier for her."

"No. She'll want it as it has always been."

I climbed in with him and the cart rocked and settled, and its springs squeaked.

"She's been a fine servant," he said. "Now just one last little journey, and she's done."

He lifted the long whip, and sighed as he flicked it towards her rump.

"Advance," he told her, as he always did, and she advanced.

We took the narrow alleyways towards the city's derelict heart. The bells on the harness jingled, her hoofsteps echoed in the dusty air. We came through the shadows into the place of public squares and parks and avenues, of palaces and offices and many-storied buildings. All doors on the buildings and all window frames were gone, all burned long ago. All glass was smashed. Lead and slate had been levered out, and marble hacked away. And paving stones had been gouged out, trees chopped down, and fences ripped apart. Opened earth and scorch marks everywhere.

Father spat.

"Thank God it can't be seen," he snapped.

The sun rose higher and the mountains shimmered in the distance in the growing heat. The tattered flags on our buildings shifted in the breeze. We moved forward step by tottering step. There was a scattering of other carts on other journeys. Hand carts, a few carts hauled by donkeys, others hauled by men. I allowed myself to lean against my father, and to remember him as he once had been.

"Do you remember," I said, "how she trotted around the garden with me on her back when I was small?"

"Yes."

"And do you remember how you used to stand with her by the gate and laugh and laugh?"

He turned his empty eyes to me.

"With who?"

"With Mother, of course."

"With *who*?"

"Advance!" I called.

I took the whip and flicked it, far too strongly.

"I'm sorry, Francesca," I called. "Take time. Slow down."

She staggered slightly, then settled and moved on.

"Let me feel your muscle," Father said.

"You felt it yesterday."

"Let me do it."

I bent my arm at the elbow, flexed, and let him feel with his shaky bony fingers.

"That's fine," he said. "It's ones like you that'll lead us back to better times."

He groaned, and leaned back against the board behind.

"That's fine," he said again. "Here. Take the reins from me."

We passed clusters of tents, neat tin-and-cardboard shacks arranged in rows. Fires smouldered. Sometimes someone waved or called our names. Once a boy ran into the road and stood before Francesca and bared his teeth and growled. She took no notice, I flicked the whip at him, and he laughed and ran away.

She led us past the potholes, through clumps of rattling weeds. We passed gangs of girls who skipped ropes and chanted names of the months in an endless round. Men hunched in twos or threes, swigging home-made liquor, smoking herbs.

We came upon the hooded storyteller, Mountfoot. He sat on a low stool, before his little audience of children. I caught the familiar notes of his voice, the familiar rhythms of it. He turned and met my eye. He mouthed to me the silent words I knew so well. I read them from his lips. *Once upon a time.* He mouthed again. *And this is how it all turned out.* Again. *But this is how it could become.* He smiled, and leaned back to his listeners, to entrance them with more stories of the not so long ago, and visions of the days to come.

We travelled on. I heard the creaking of her bones within the creaking of the cart.

"It isn't far," I called to her.

But our progress was slow. I tried to look through the city to the open space on the other side, but there were still so many buildings, so many interlinking streets.

"The potato trench?" muttered Father.

"I remembered it."

"The water butt?"

"I repaired it."

We approached the place of market stalls, the place to which most of our journeys led us. Our friends called out.

"So what have you brought for us today?"

"Now we'll get some decent onions!"

"Come and trade for these delicious bangers."

"Just don't ask where they come from!"

Then they saw the struggles of Francesca and the emptiness of the cart, and they lowered their heads and let us pass.

Bernardo the baker caught up with us, carrying slices of soda bread.

"How is he?" he asked me softly.

"He's fine!" snapped Father. "Better to ask him how the garden is. That's what he has to care for now."

Bernardo smiled. He gave me another piece of bread. He stroked Francesca.

"The tiger?" he asked.

I nodded.

"It still survives?"

"So we believe."

"But very old, I think."

"Yes, very old."

"Ah, well. And then?"

I looked away.

"Another donkey?" he whispered.

"Perhaps. If we are careful", he says. "If the potatoes grow well. If …"

"Advance!" snapped Father.

"Those chillis you brought," Bernardo murmured. "They were delicious, so fiery. Your berries were so sweet. You're so good at what you do. Here, take more bread."

"Advance!"

I thanked Bernardo, and on we went.

Then he dozed. I thought he'd stay awake, on this of all days. Francesca slowed, stumbled, steadied again. We followed the boulevards, we passed through the triumphal arch. Children played happily in the dirt there, making a pyramid. Three stood arm-in-arm in line, two were climbing up onto their shoulders, and another watched and waited. The pyramid toppled and fell, and the children laughed. I thought of jumping down and running to join them. They saw me, they waved, one called my name.

"Come on!" he called.

They knew I couldn't. I had become a man to them now. They stood together again, and climbed again, and didn't watch as we went on.

The stench woke Father up.

A plundered carcass, seething with flies.

"Ach!" he gagged.

"Donkey?" he said.

"Yes."

"Look away, Francesca!" he called.

It lay there by the roadside, half ripped apart.

"Those fools!" he said.

Some thought that this was right, to allow their ancient donkeys to simply fall. Why not let the poor beast sleep, they said. Why insist on yet another journey for no reward? Vermin and the desperate will take the flesh. Dogs will take the bones. The rest will quickly turn like us to rubble, dust and dirt. What does it matter now?

That was despair, my father said. We must care for our animals as we always have, right up to their last breath.

"We should have put the blinkers on her," he said.

Then he suddenly stood up and said, "But no!" and he spread his arms out wide just like he used to do, and he called out,

"Look beyond it to the beauty, Francesca! Use your lovely eyes! Look at how splendid this world has been, and is, and how splendid it will be again."

The cart rocked wildly. Francesca tottered.

I drew Father back down to his seat. He clenched his fists and thrust them at his eyes.

"*Is* it splendid?" he asked me after a time.

"You know it's not, not now."

"No?"

"No."

"Is there beauty in it?"

"Yes. As you used to say, it is in everything. Remember?"

"Advance!" he said.

We advanced, through this city that resembled a city after war. But there had been no war, not here. War had happened far away, beyond the shining mountains and the hidden sea. We had sent those beautiful glistening aeroplanes to it, those that had streamed above me in my infancy. We had sent those trucks and tanks that thundered in exciting formation through the streets and squares, those bright-eyed young men who waved and winked at we children as they bravely marched across our squares. We'd given everything, we were told. We'd done our duty. And look, hadn't we come through? Hadn't we been saved?

The closest thing to war in this place had been the bitter time of rebellion afterwards, when the men of my father's age streamed through the steel gates, stormed the unprotected offices and palaces, strode through the great corridors, the state rooms, the drawing rooms with bare walls, the vaults with their steel doors gaping open, to find just emptiness, and all inhabitants except the lowest servants gone. The city could have become a place of death and danger, a place that seethed with cut-throats, brigands and the crazed. And yes there was the dreadful time, when Mother, Father and I sheltered in our cellar and Francesca shivered in her stable, as fires raged outside and ancient feuds were resurrected and battles fought for plundered trinkets. But there was no way to take vengeance on those who truly deserved it. No purpose in attacking those like us who had nothing. No point in becoming lord of a heap of broken stones.

The city became sad, not perilous. All we feared now was hunger, occasional outbursts of madness, the wild beasts that each year prowled deeper into the city, the snakes that slithered through the wastelands and gardens, and those rumoured gangs who were said to haunt the darkest places, ready to leap out and take us for our flesh. And we feared simple illness, and the simplest of infections, like the one that took my mother rapidly away.

And memory, of course. Some of us feared that most of all, for the dread of truly knowing what we'd lost.

Francesca staggered. I thought she was about to drop. I pulled on the reins.

"Rest," I told her. "Take some time."

"Where are we?"

"By the cathedral, Father."

It was doorless, windowless. Its steeple had toppled through its own roof. It was home to buzzards and bats and the clan of the mad who chanted at night and said that something kind looks out at us from nothingness. Ha! I climbed down and stood by Francesca. I took the pail of water to her and she drank. I held my face to hers. Swallows flicked and dashed, and eagles soared high above.

"Do *you* remember?" I whispered. "Do *you* remember how she laughed as we trotted through the garden?"

The singing of many birds rang down on us. It sounded like like a mockery of us, then like the music of our grieving.

"Do *you* remember how she said they simply sing for joy?" I said. "And that they will continue to sing for joy long after we are gone?"

Father flicked the whip.

"Where are you?" he said. "Where are we?"

I felt Francesca's warm breath on me.

"And do you remember the night she died?" I whispered. "You were so warm and comforting as I lay on you, while he just drank, and howled at the unbothered moon?"

"Where the hell are you? Where the hell am I?"

There were more children nearby. Why didn't I just go to them? Why didn't I just run right out towards the mountains as so many were said to do, to live a life of foraging and wandering? Why didn't I just flee?

"Where?" said Father. "Where?"

He flicked the whip. It fell across us both. I turned to him.

"Here!" I snapped. "Here, damn you!"

And then I shuddered, for there it was beyond him, the summit of the pale blue tent, above the rooftops and the ruins, almost blending in the distance with the pale blue sky.

I climbed back up to him.

"I can't do it," I said.

"You must!"

He grabbed the reins again.

"Advance!" he said.

She could hardly walk, but she staggered onward, entering the desolate alleyways that would lead us to the wasteland at the city's edge.

"Advance! We are almost at the circus!"

*

Perhaps someone had told Arrowsmith that we were on our way. He was waiting for us. The breeze blew in from the plains. His fair hair swirled and his red robes danced. The huge slumped tent behind him shuddered and flapped. The shacks and caravans of the clowns and trapeze artists were scattered around it. Behind it were the hidden cages of the few remaining beasts.

"I can give nothing," said Arrowsmith.

"Nothing?" I said.

"But I will take her, as I always have."

He stood at her side.

"Once we could have given a bag of silver coins for one as beautiful as you," he said. "But who wants to pay to see strongmen who can't lift, flyers who can't fly, horses that can't dance? Only the children come now. They creep in beneath the canvas, they lie in the shadows beneath the seats. They try to stay secret but they can't stop themselves from cheering."

He smiled.

"We let them stay. They are an audience, after all."

"Her name is Francesca," said Father.

"She will be very sweet."

He looked into my eyes and laughed.

"A year's free entry for you both, perhaps."

He saw my tears falling.

"It is as it has always been," he said. "I take the ancient and the lame. Francesca keeps us going a little longer, until it's over, or until better times arrive. You turn back to your life again. Shall I unfasten her?"

I didn't answer.

"Look at her," he said. "She doesn't have the strength to make it home again. Shall I unfasten her?"

"Yes!" snapped Father.

I climbed down and stepped in front of Arrowsmith. I unfastened the belts and harness. I pulled the cart away from her. She snorted, flicked her mane, shuffled her hooves.

"So familiar," said Arrowsmith. "A moment of being young again right at the very end!"

"Where is the tiger?" I asked him.

"Nearby. Don't worry. It will be fast. Despite everything, he is still capable of great and sudden savagery. Would you like to stay with her?"

"No!" snapped Father.

"Some do," said Arrowsmith. "They wish to see it all through to the end."

"No!"

I kissed her cheek. I stroked the smooth hair that lay upon her head. I felt the perfectly shaped skull beneath. I felt her breath falling across me. I whispered farewell and that I would always remember her. Arrowsmith lifted my hands from her and led her towards the far side of the tent.

"Take the shafts!" said Father.

I waited. I stared into the distance, followed with my eyes the dusty roads and tracks that led into the emptiness.

"You must take them! There is much to do!"

I listened to the breeze, the birds. I watched the sun, already falling back towards the horizon.

Then came the tiger's roar, Francesca's cry, the snapping of her bones.

"Take them!"

I let my tears fall.

"Take them!"

The whip fell across me. I caught it, pulled it from him, and flung it away. I waited.

"Yes," he said. "I remember her."

"Good."

I crouched, lifted the shafts, stood up again.

I was still young yet I had become a man. I had memory and I had sight and I was strong. I knew that all could change.

"Advance!" he said, and I turned back to the city and advanced.

DAVID ALMOND IS THE AUTHOR OF *SKELLIG*, *THE TRUE TALE OF THE MONSTER BILLY DEAN* AND MANY OTHER NOVELS, STORIES AND PLAYS. HIS LATEST BOOK IS *THE BOY WHO SWAM WITH PIRANHAS*. IN 2010 HE WAS GIVEN THE HANS CHRISTIAN ANDERSEN AWARD. HE IS PROFESSOR OF CREATIVE WRITING AT BATH SPA UNIVERSITY.

RED ALERT

Suzanne Moore

If you are a woman of a certain inclination, google "Calm Down Dear" and wind back the footage to April of last year. David Cameron, more cocksure than he is at present, directs the phrase at Labour MP Angela Eagle during Prime Minister's Questions in a debate over health policy. He says it more than once, so bowled over is he with his own Wildean wit. It's a shame really since it's actually a catchphrase of that peculiarly mega-loaded film director, Michael Winner. Still, this being the House of Commons, Cameron's own frontbench are convulsed. Beside him is a man not quite as beside himself as the others – Nick Clegg, looking as he so often does, wistfully wishing he were elsewhere. The Liberal Democrat leader may have few senior women in his own party but in that hollow where his heart used to be, he intuits this is not the way to address female colleagues.

Many of us do. Many of us don't feel calm but angry and perturbed that the humour embraced by Fragrant Dave is that of a previous generation (Benny Hill?). That may well be what being a conservative means: conserving the worst of things as well as the best of them. I speak, of course, as a humourless "feminazi". Anyone who takes offence at being patronised should "grow some" as they say. Tory MP Louise Mensch's visible frustration at not being moved up party ranks and subsequent resignation meant that, despite her high profile, duller yet controversial men like Jeremy Hunt are still seen as less risky promotions. Our supposedly modernising Prime Minister, who once aimed to appoint women to a third of cabinet positions, ensured that out of twenty-two senior jobs available in the latest reshuffle, only four were given to women. That aspiration, for representative democracy to be more representative, went very quickly out of the window. As did his promises about the environment. We shall have to hope that climate change doesn't really happen and that women just try a little harder. Keep calm and carry on. You can't have everything. Indeed half the population already know that and some of us have been seeing red for quite some time about just how quickly we are slipping backwards. According to the equality campaigning organisation, the Fawcett Society, we are currently ranked fifty-seventh in the world when it comes to cabinet-level posts. That might be worth thinking about as Samantha Cameron shows us how to wear Zara or Michelle Obama has to tell us about how much she loves Obama.

Does it matter? Just possibly. Every statistic available shows that women and children are being hit hardest by this recession. Women are losing more jobs than men in the public sector (65% of public sector workers are female) and the services they consume the most are also being cut back. Many women now find themselves as unpaid carers with no remuneration whatsoever.

Meanwhile, a parliament of men can still legislate over the bodies of women. Indeed Hunt, the new Secretary of State for Health, wants the limit on abortion to be twelve weeks. Despite polls in support of women's right to choose, the law is whittled away by continual attacks on time limits. A tiny number of women have abortions past twenty-four weeks, 147 in the year before last. Late abortions for "social reasons" do occur, and if you can read some of those case notes you have a stronger stomach than I. If you are raped by a member of your own family and then beaten with an iron bar while pregnant, you may well not want that baby. Abortion, we are told, is an issue of conscience. No, it is an issue of control. It is fundamentally about whether the state can control the bodies of women.

Obviously, not all women feel the same way about this because we are all different – you know, rather like men. Funny chaps, women! Many of us don't fight for more women in power in politics or in the board room because these women somehow speak for all of us but because it is simply insane that such a power imbalance remains. At the current rate of change, the Fawcett Society estimates a child born today will be drawing her pension before she sees equal numbers of men and women in the House of Commons.

Either meritocracy works or it doesn't. We can conclude women are not as good at running banks or government departments or that they just aren't "hungry" enough. We can say it might better if we didn't go in for the baby malarkey, which is a real downer on career prospects.

Or we could be cold, hard and livid that this remains the case. All those tired but wired woman that you see with a briefcase and a snatched bag of M&S ready meals. Are they really having it all? It's not just the double shift of work and domestic duties that women do. There is now a third shift – we must keep ourselves sexually attractive forever. This requires more "work" in the form of surgery. When breasts became bouncy castles for male enjoyment, the imploding implant scandal was waiting to happen. Every woman who has it done claims they are doing it for themselves, their self-worth residing in a body to be used by others. If cutting yourself up as "empowerment" seems a little too much, then just inject yourself with poisonous Botox. I always say the best filler is cake.

These are the most conservative times for women I can remember. But why are we not saying "Enough, already"? Why are we not telling our inbred overlords that we are not as nice as we look? Partly because we are afraid of our own anger. It's not a pretty sight. Seeing red and letting go is, for many women, a dangerous activity. We are only ever a few HRT pills away from being a monstrous regiment. Women's rage is also never seen as what we say it is actually about. It is inchoate, unreadable and uncontrollable.

It is, of course, also totally thrilling. Feminism as "a movement" has collapsed in the West, in the way of most collective struggles. We can call this postmodern, we can say neoliberalism appropriated feminism simply so that wage slaves could equally be male and female, but it's not so simple. It hasn't gone away. The recasting of feminism as only of interest to a few middle-class white women is a media trope. Outbursts of anger, politicised and scalpel sharp, are everywhere we look. The Respect party leader Salma Yaqoob recently resigned over issues of "trust". Clearly she could no longer tolerate her colleague George Galloway's attitudes towards women and rape, given his remarks about WikiLeaks founder Julian Assange. The allegations of rape against Assange were dismissed as a plot or simply poor "sexual etiquette". The sight of the hard left coalescing around Julian Assange, is indeed sore. Yet again, those most vociferous about human rights seem somehow not to see women's rights as part of the same conversation.

Elsewhere, Pussyriot, young and able to use the net to spread the word about Russian President Vladimir's Putin's slide into dictatorship with the backing of the Orthodox Church, achieved far more than earnest politicking has done by performing their "Punk Prayer" for less than a minute in knitted balaclavas. "What we have in common is impudence, politically loaded lyrics, the importance of feminist discourse ...", they said. That three of them are in prison for two years is a disgrace. That even Dmitri Medvedev, the Russian prime minister, is calling for their release shows their message is hitting where it hurts.

Women are, of course, hurt whenever they stand up to repressive regimes. Sometimes by their own "comrades". The widely documented sexual assaults on many young Egyptian women who joined their "brothers" in the Arab Spring protests show that the position of women remains vulnerable. Nonetheless, women continue to remind us that feminism isn't all Naomi Wolf-style fanny gazing. Look at Nobel Peace Prize winner, the Liberian Leymah Gbowee, who brought together women determined to find peace in a country torn apart by religious divides and civil war through demonstrations, sit-ins, even sex strikes. "We have to be our own Gandhis, our own Kings, our own Mandelas," she said. What started as groups of women just sitting together in the fish market in white T-shirts led to the eventual demise of the war criminal Charles Taylor and the election of a female president.

While some kinds of feminism meld well with the logic of late capitalism, others challenge it. The stark facts are as follows. Wherever women become educated, they have fewer children and when they become financially independent, the model of monogamous marriage breaks down. Freedom is neither easy or easily defined. And we must be alert to how easily it can be threatened.

In this country, the red warning lights were flashing at the last election when women were largely invisible except as trophy wives. Women's "issues" are still something to be tacked onto another ministerial department. The ideas of quotas is still abhorrent to those born to rule: white men. Those who refute social engineering are themselves the products of the best social engineering money can buy: public school and then Oxbridge.

Oh yes, I know there are token women and the Top Trump always remains Margaret Thatcher. Having often featured myself as a token woman, I find the role an insult in 2012. At a dinner with Iain Duncan Smith, the Secretary of State for Work and Pensions charged with reforming the benefits system, I heard him telling the assembled guests what it was like being a single parent, I sat silent, waiting to be asked my views, as I am one. A scarlet flush was spreading across my chest. This was far from post-coital colour. My blood was rising. The anger could not be swallowed. I left the table.

This kind of action is not fashionable. We cloak our vitriol in humour. I get it. I do it too. Caitlin Moran's bestselling *How to Be a Woman* is a brilliantly funny read because it is so warm and not really very angry towards men. We can all be dudes. But former Sex Pistol John Lydon's chant , "anger is an energy", is still my *cri de coeur*.

The cliché is that female anger is always turned inwards rather than outwards into despair. We are angry with ourselves for not being happier, not being loved properly and not having the ideal body shape – that of a Brazilian transsexual. We are angry that men do not do enough. We are angry at work where we are underpaid and overlooked.

This anger can be neatly channelled and outsourced to make someone a fat profit. Are your hormones okay? Do you need a nice bath? Some sex tips and an internet date? What if, contrary to *Sex and the City*, new shoes do not fill the hole in your soul? What if you aspire to another model of womanhood than the mute but beautifully groomed Kate Middleton? What if your anguish is not illogical but actually bloody spot on?

Maybe your man can read *Men's Health* and use the "11 ways to deal with an angry woman" advice. Eye contact and admitting you are were wrong come into it! Who knew?

Those more vulnerable, the women in our midst going without dinner so the kids can eat, are they going to be helped by talking of anger as an issue of intimacy? The Etonian clones abandoned these women long ago and are producing policies that directly target them. Those hazard lights should be flashing: women can't be wooed to vote by being shown the nice handbag of a politician's wife.

I see my daughters' generation written off as pretty much everything I took for granted is being systematically stripped away from them. Jobs, housing, free education. The expectation that these young women would have the same choice or more even than their mothers is being shattered. They have less.

This is why so many of us are seeing red. The signs flicker all around, whichever side of the political divide we are on. We see red, not as a mist but clear and scarlet. Cherish it, for this is how the future will be made. As Gwobee says "Anger is like water: the shape it takes comes from the container you put it in." Let it flow.

SUZANNE MOORE IS A JOURNALIST WHO HAS WRITTEN FOR EVERYTHING FROM *MARXISM TODAY* TO *THE MAIL ON SUNDAY*. SHE IS THE AUTHOR OF TWO BOOKS OF COLLECTED JOURNALISM AND IS CURRENTLY A COLUMNIST FOR *THE GUARDIAN*. SUZANNE HAS THREE CHILDREN AND NO HOBBIES.

SAINT KENTIGERN'S

Anthony Horowitz

Evelyn Thomas, author of *Boris the Bear*, *Boris Wins the Day*, *Boris Meets the Queen* and thirty-two more books with Boris in the title, stepped out of the taxi and found himself in front of a village school that was almost absurdly sweet; old red bricks and ivy that reminded him of his own childhood, a playground with swings and see-saw, tiled roof and double-height windows. He was in a bad mood. It was a very hot day and it had taken him much longer than he had anticipated to travel from Notting Hill Gate in London to this empty spot near the Suffolk coast – by train from Liverpool Street, a change at Ipswich and then a taxi (why not a waiting delegation?) from Woodbridge. He would talk to his assistant as soon as he got back.

There was no-one to meet him here either. Evelyn scowled in the sunlight as the taxi reversed and rattled up the narrow country lane, disappearing round the corner as if it had been swallowed up by the grass and hedgerows. It was rather odd for a village school to be a quarter of a mile outside the nearest village. How did the children get here in the morning? He supposed there must be a school bus. Health and safety, of course, would prevent them from walking. Anyway, that wasn't his concern. More to the point, he wondered how the school had ever managed to reach him, sending him an invitation for an author visit. And why had he accepted it?

The truth was that Evelyn Thomas had more or less invented himself, visiting school after school after school with his stories of a Russian bear with a smattering of English and even less common sense, having hilarious adventures that somehow always came right in the end. He had written the first one in his early thirties, shortly after his advertising agency had collapsed. Aimed squarely at the primary school market, it had sold precisely 3,000 copies and wouldn't even have covered its advance if the advance hadn't been so small in the first place. It was amazing, really, that the publisher had stuck by him. His original contract had been for three books and although the next two had hardly done much better, they had extended it, bringing the total to five. Nobody had reviewed *Boris the Bear*. The publishers refused to pay for advertising. The shops were uninterested. But as Evelyn had quickly discovered, self-publicity was the easy answer. There was an author trail, a dotted line that connected all the schools in the UK. He would actually be paid to talk to the children for one hour and at the end, after applause and a cup of tea, he could sit down and sell thirty or forty books. It was, as he saw it, a win–win situation.

He had quickly found that the more schools he visited, the more success he had. It was as if there were a sort of playground word-of-mouth across the country that grew louder and stronger with every visit. By the time the fifth book (*Boris Goes Bananas*) came out, he was doing as many as eleven schools a week. His on-site sales, signed with a flourish and a badly drawn bear, remained about the same but he became aware of a knock-on effect. Boris the Bear was making a name for himself in the local shops of every place he visited. Suddenly he was in the *Bookseller*, fairly low down on the bestseller list but there all the same and, once he had established this foot-hold (or was it a paw-hold?), he had instantly begun to climb. He was progressing through the bookshops too, turning face up on the shelf, then moving into "Recommended", finally finding himself centre table. His publishers noticed and invited him for lunch. A week later, there was a six-book contract in front of him. Evelyn got himself a new agent. The agent agreed the contract but doubled the advance. The publishers didn't mind at all. Without anyone noticing how or when it had happened, the bear had become something of a national institution. A major newspaper had even joked that he was the second most famous Boris in the country.

But with thirty-five books behind him, thinning hair, a bad back and heavy black spectacles, Evelyn Thomas was enjoying the books rather less than when he had started them ... and even then his inspiration had frankly been financial rather than creative. Aged fifty, he had no children of his own. He was a small, rather plump man and chose his clothes carefully to disguise the distinctly pregnant curve of his stomach. He still smoked between pages and this, along with his sedentary lifestyle, gave him the appearance of someone you might meet in a funeral parlour – its manager or, more likely, its client.

Saint Kentigern's. He read the name on a wooden board, painted immaculately, in gold. Head teacher: Miss Moira Whitchurch. Well, at least that was something. Evelyn was in many ways an old-fashioned man and he much preferred the straightforward Miss to the far more common Ms, which displayed so many assumptions along with its absent two letters. He wiped his brow. It really was hot. He couldn't remember it being as bad as this when he left London.

He heard a scraping sound, a rhymthic scratch, scratch, scratch, then a pause, then the same pattern repeated and, as he looked up, he saw a man coming round the side of the building, brushing the ground with a heavy, wooden broom. He was wasting his time. There wasn't so much as a leaf or a single chewing gum wrapper in sight. In fact the whole school had a pristine quality that quite belied its role in life. The man doing the cleaning was dressed in grey overalls. He was about ten years older than Evelyn, long-faced with a beak-like nose. Evelyn started. Surely the two of them had met before? No. That was impossible. He had never been here and he didn't make a habit of patronising school caretakers.

The man looked up briefly, breaking the pattern of his work, and Evelyn smiled to himself. Now he remembered. He had a slight resemblance to a writer he had once known, Max Bentley, author of the very successful sci fi series, "Potty Planets" and a self-satisfied tosser if ever there was one. The two of them had rubbed up against each other at Bath and Cheltenham, two of the long line-up of literary festivals that Evelyn had added to his annual rounds. Max Bentley had stopped writing about six years ago. He had simply hung up his pen and vanished from the scene. Evelyn planned to do exactly the same as soon as he had made enough cash.

"Mr Thomas?"

The speaker was a short, fair-haired woman with startling, blue eyes who had somehow come out of the school without him seeing her. She was about thirty, he would have said, attractive in a careless, thrown together sort of way, dressed in bright colours with cheap jewellery.

"That's me," he said, smiling in the way he had smiled a hundred times before.

"We're so pleased you came. The children are such fans of Boris the Bear. They've been so excited. Do please come this way." She was already leading him into the school, ignoring the scratch, scratch, scratch of the caretaker who had promptly returned to his work. "We're only small so it's very special when we can manage to snag authors like yourself. Your books are always in and out of the library. Saint Kentigern … do you know him? The patron saint of salmon and bullies. He's also known as Saint Mungo. I believe there's only one other school in the country with the same name."

She prattled on as they passed through heavy glass doors and into a corridor, empty of people now but still filled with the echoes of the children who had passed through. There was an assortment of small cups and trophies behind a glass panel, coats and jerseys on hooks, strange art objects made of cardboard and papier maché on tables, and everywhere bright, jagged paintings in pastel, oil, crayon and watercolour contrasting with the austere wood panelling and the black and white tiled floor.

"How was the journey from London?" Miss Whitchurch asked.

"Long." Evelyn was in a bad mood and hoped he hadn't betrayed it with the one-word answer. Whatever his feelings, he knew that it was essential always to be nice. He looked around, expecting to see a receptionist and a signing-in book. There were schools these days that wouldn't even let you in without ID. But it seemed the head teacher had decided to dispense with this formality.

"It is a bit of a haul. Would you like coffee or tea?" She hadn't slowed down. It was as if she expected him to refuse.

"Well …"

"The children are already in class." She had answered for him. "Will an hour be all right? After that, you'll hear the bell for lunch."

Before he could speak, she had ushered him into a small room where twenty children sat behind old-fashioned desks, the sort with a slanting top that opened on a hinge. There were a few shelves with books, the inevitable globe, bits and pieces scavenged from the fields and, at the back, a picture of an old man, in a golden frame. He looked like an Eastern European, with grey hair and a beard, his hand pressed against his chest. Presumably this was the saint that the head teacher had mentioned.

The children were all wearing uniform, pastel blue blazers and black trousers or dresses. Evelyn's first impression was that, like the school, they were remarkably sweet and attractive; twelve boys and eight girls all aged about nine or ten years old. Only a couple of the children were black, ethnic … whatever the word was you were supposed to use. That was hardly surprising in the middle of Suffolk. What did strike him as odd was that, although there was no adult in the room, they had all been waiting in complete silence, their hands folded in front of them, their faces attentive. Even as he came in, there was a stir of excitement but none of the shouting or restlessness that he had experienced in other schools. Some of the children were holding his books … a good sign. He would have recognised the front covers or even the spines instantly, at thirty paces.

Miss Whitchurch led him to a table in front of an old-fashioned blackboard. The room was painted bright white to the extent that the reflected sunlight, pouring in through high, sash windows, almost dazzled him. It was very hot.

"Good morning, children," the head teacher said. "We are very, very lucky to have Mr Evelyn Thomas with us today. Who has read a *Boris the Bear* book?" Every hand in the class went up. Evelyn was pleased. He'd visited inner city schools where only two or three of the kids (and none of the teachers) had read any of his work. "Well, today, you can find out everything you want to know about these wonderful stories. Mr Thomas will talk to you for a while and then I'm sure he'll be delighted to answer your questions." She glanced at him as if to ask if he was happy with this arrangement and he nodded back. It occurred to him that everything was happening a bit quickly, but then he had no reason to linger. Do the usual talk. Answer the usual questions. Sign books. Then back on the train to London. He really wondered what he was doing here. "Do go ahead, Mr Thomas." Miss Whitchurch stepped aside and sat down, folding her legs neatly in front of her.

"Good morning," Evelyn began. He paused and smiled at the twenty solemn, attentive faces gazing up at him. "I wonder how many have you wondered what it must be like to live in Russia and to come all the way to a country like England. It must be very strange. But it's even stranger and more difficult if you happen to be a bear!"

He had uttered the words so many times before that he almost hated himself for speaking them again and he had to work hard to make them sound fresh. It often occurred to him that modern writers had to be actors – or actually stand-up comedians – delivering jokes, insights, shared experiences and anecdotes to different audiences week after week. The only difference was that stand-up comedians could change their material. He was stuck with the same patter week after week. Even as he found himself launching into his first set piece –"Life in the Kamchatka

Peninsula" – he had to suppress the sense of self-disgust. There were plenty of things he would rather be doing now, at least one of them with his new assistant, who was twenty-three and seemed willing enough … not that he would share that particular thought with a bunch of ten-year-olds.

He paused to wipe the sweat off his forehead with the back of his hand. Miss Whitchurch had managed to bypass the tea and coffee but surely she could have managed a glass of bloody water. Well, best to get this over with. Most of the talk was second-hand, drawn from the stories themselves … all the scrapes that Boris had got into. After all, at the end of the day, he didn't have that much to add. He sat in a room and he wrote books. What else was there to say? For Evelyn, this was an exercise in advertising. Buy my books. Tell your friends. Leave me alone.

There was an old-fashioned clock at the back of the room. He had begun at eleven o' clock. He stopped at a quarter to twelve exactly. Fifteen minutes for questions and he was out of here.

The children applauded politely but without the sense of enthusiasm or even childishness that he had experienced elsewhere. He found himself discomforted by the way they were looking at him. What was it? What was it that made them so very slightly sinister? Finally, it dawned on him. At every school he had ever visited, the children had reacted to his talk in different ways. There had been those who were absorbed. Those who laughed uproariously. Those who were frankly bored and fidgeted. But this lot were all identical, watching him with the same, polite interest. God! What did they feed them on out here? Or was this what came of living in the middle of nowhere?

"Well, that was very interesting," Miss Whitchurch said as if they'd just had a talk on home safety by the local fire brigade rather than an audience with one of the most successful children's writers in the country. "Now, who has the first question?" She paused. "Hermione?"

A girl in the second row had put up her hand. "Where do you get your ideas?" she asked.

"That's a very good question!" Miss Whitchurch turned to Evelyn for an answer.

It was a blindingly obvious question, actually. He had only been asked it about a thousand times before. But Evelyn did his best, talking about the leather notebook he kept beside his bed (in fact it didn't exist) and all the thoughts and experiences he wrote down before he went to sleep. "Ideas are everywhere!" he said. "If I see a man running for a bus, I ask myself why he's late and where he's going and that might suggest a story. And of course, if he falls over in a puddle, that might be something I put in a book."

The notion of an adult slipping in a puddle often got a laugh. This crowd remained silent.

"How did you get the name for Boris?"

The boy next to her had asked this and he couldn't have been listening because, during his talk, Evelyn had already explained where the name came from. This often happened and usually he would ignore the error and answer the question anyway but today he was feeling peeved. "I think I already told you that," he said.

"That's right, William," Miss Whitchurch said, reproachfully and then, as if to brighten the mood: "Can anyone tell Mr Thomas where he got the name from?" Every hand in the room went up. "Raj?"

"He stole it!"

"No, no, Raj. Mr Thomas borrowed the name from a famous book, *Boris Godunov*. One day, perhaps, we'll look at it in class. Who has the next question?"

"What's your favourite book?" This came from a ginger-haired boy at the back.

"I think I like *Boris and the Burglar* best," Evelyn replied. This was a lie. It wasn't a very good book at all. Even his publishers had wondered if the formula wasn't becoming a touch stale, although none of them had said so directly. That was why he was promoting it now. Twenty copies here, thirty there. It was important to nudge the sales. "I had a lot of fun writing it and I think it's got some great jokes."

"Why did you fire your agent?" The speaker was a tiny girl in the front row, her feet swinging at least an inch above the ground, fair haired with stick-like arms folded in front of her.

Well, that was an odd question and one that Evelyn had never been asked before, certainly not during a school visit. But the story had been reported in the *Bookseller* and Evelyn assumed they must have found it on the net before he arrived. "It was just a business thing," he said. "We had different ideas about the books and I thought it was time to move on."

"But she was very upset," the little girl insisted. "She represented you for years and years and after the books got successful you just sent her a two-line text!"

"It wasn't a text. It was a telex. They didn't have texting then," the boy next to her said.

"Well done, Jonathan!" Miss Whitchurch murmured.

"It was all about money," a plump boy with freckles added. "The new agent said he could get a better deal."

This was true – but it was getting out of hand. Evelyn turned to the head teacher for support but she sat where she was, expecting him to respond. He felt a trickle of sweat down the side of his neck. Couldn't they at least open one of the windows? "I don't really think I want to talk about my business," he said. "And do you think I could have a glass of water?"

"Why did your wife divorce you?"

Christ! That really was too close to the bone. The speaker was an angelic boy with a neat, blonde fringe, the sort who could have stood in the front row of any self-respecting choir.

"Now wait a minute …", Evelyn began.

"Did you hurt her a lot?" the boy asked as a follow-up question.

"Has Caroline been here?" Evelyn asked. His ex-wife had moved to Norwich, now that he thought about it, and that wasn't so far away. If she had broken the terms of her settlement she'd be hearing from him. There had been an iron-plated confidentiality agreement bolted in.

"Why did you have so many affairs?"

That was too much. Evelyn turned angrily to the head teacher. "I'm not prepared to answer any of these questions!" he snapped. "And I have to say, I've never met kids who would even have been allowed …"

But the questions were still coming, one overlapping with the next, shouted at him from the different parts of the classroom.

"How often do you make your editor cry?"

"Why do you say such nasty things about other writers?"

"You stole the idea for Boris the Bear. Why don't you just admit it?"

Evelyn couldn't let that one go past. "That's not true," he exclaimed. "There was a similarity but …"

"You have tons of money. Why don't you ever give any to charity?"

"Why don't you pay any tax?"

"Why do you hate so many people?"

"What's your favourite recreational drug?"

Evelyn wanted to leave. He had made his mind up to leave even as the questions exploded around him. But the strength had drained out of him. He felt himself trapped in the sunlight, pinned in the heat and the glare as these horrible children continued their shrill interrogation, their unbroken voices not loud and yet somehow piercing.

"How can you go on writing books when you think they're rubbish?"

"How many hours a day do you spend watching porn on the internet?"

The saint in his gold frame seemed to have turned his head so that his grey eyes were locked into Evelyn's. What was happening to him? There was a terrible pain in his chest and he was sure he was having a heart attack.

The questions had become a cacophony, thundering in his ears, and he realised that he was locked into place, his feet as secure as the roots of a tree. He tried to turn his head but his neck had petrified. "Why ...?" "When?" "Who?" "How often ...?" Every child in the room was shouting at him. All he could see was their mouths and eyes. They had become a blur and suddenly, with a rush of complete horror, he felt his bladder release itself. As the liquid poured down behind his trousers, he slumped forward and collapsed to the ground.

*

Some time later.

Garry Baker, the popular presenter of BBC's *Let's Have a Laugh* steps out of a taxi and stands in the afternoon sun. He is here as part of a nationwide tour, promoting his autobiography – *Garry with Two Rs*. At the age of just twenty-five, he has little to write about but that hasn't put off the many thousands of fans who have bought his new book. As he waits, a little impatiently, for someone to greet him, he hears the sound of a brush, sweeping the playground ... even though it seems to him that there is nothing actually to sweep. A moment later, a man appears, dressed in grey overalls with thinning hair, a large stomach and heavy, black spectacles. Garry has never seen anyone so absorbed in his work. The man is sweeping as if his life depends on it.

But here's the head teacher coming out to greet him. Garry Baker raises a hand and, with a smile fixed to his face, walks into the school.

ANTHONY HOROWITZ HAS VISITED MANY SCHOOLS AS ONE OF THE COUNTRY'S BEST-KNOWN CHILDREN'S WRITERS. HE ALSO WRITES FOR TELEVISION AND FILM AND HIS FIRST ADULT NOVEL, A SHERLOCK HOLMES STORY — *THE HOUSE OF SILK* — HAS JUST BEEN PUBLISHED IN PAPERBACK BY ORION. HIS NEW NOVEL, *OBLIVION*, IS PUBLISHED BY WALKER BOOKS.

THANK GOD FOR BLOOD

Alice Oswald

thank god for hospital-cathedrals plate glass doors far up white
strip lights lifts to the top floor and afterwards heaven

thank god for the window its dimness thank god for crowds
each person looking for his lost

thank god in the central corridor white twilight choirs are
walking with instruments white sheets pale hands two tablets
in the mouth white curtains closed

thank god for singing for syringe in the vein white sleeves rolled up

thank god for the sleep whose ears grow used to the bleep bleep
bleep

thank god for a screaming man thank god for one woman naked
thank god for another one trembling resembling above all a
nettle and a child as thin as a music stand now fully extended
adjusted to herself and no other

thank god for these god-forsaken ferns

thank god for the on off switch phosphorus face white wings
    white coats asleep on a hook where cleaners sweep thank
    god for the moon in white cotton thank god for humans
    anonymous standing under the white-cold eyes of the stars'
    closed-circuit cameras taking a fag-break thinking thank god
    for the hope coming out through our lips in a tepid cloud

thank god for the soul being buried in nourishment like a potato
    thank god for the mind kept in behind hair-flaps not listening
    thank god for us all when you cut us open being dressed in
    matching red

for the cloth of the heart for the fine bright thread for the blind
    work of the blood for the wound that made so much man
    thank god for the bandage

ALICE OSWALD HAS PUBLISHED SIX BOOKS OF POETRY AND A NUMBER OF SMALL,
EXPERIMENTAL COLLECTIONS. SHE HAS WON VARIOUS AWARDS INCLUDING THE
T.S.ELIOT, THE HAWTHORNDEN AND THE TED HUGHES.

PREPOSITIONS

Lionel Shriver

September 9, 2011

Dear Sarah,

I apologize for the formality of a letter, but I can't trust myself to get this out over a glass of wine, especially while still unsure what I want to say.

Trust that I've treasured your friendship always. On that hiking trip through the Sinai desert when we all met, what brought our two couples together was a shared disinclination to complain. Other tourists whined ceaselessly about the heat and the food, but we four were intrepid. When you broke out in suppurating cold sores from too much sun, despite the injury to your vanity you trooped on as if nothing were the matter. Consequently, I'd hate for this letter itself to seem a complaint – but then, maybe it is a complaint.

Your husband died *in* 9/11. My husband died *on* 9/11. So much has ensued from those prepositions, a single one-letter variation in the alphabet.

Oddly, your story is at least as vivid to me as my own, since I've heard you recount it so many times at dinner parties. It's the story that everyone wants to hear. How the offices of David's investment bank had only recently moved to the 89th floor – a step up in every sense, but if only they'd stayed on the 37th David would probably have survived; that day brambled with *if only*s. The PA announcement that everyone in the South Tower should return to their desks, which lost seven precious minutes to escape before the second plane hit. Your final conversation with your husband. His report that the only working stairwell was billowing with smoke. His intention to head with several dozen others to the roof. The door to the roof being locked, though you only learned that later. The helicopters that never came.

Yet I've told my story seldom. It doesn't feed local appetites. So allow me, this once. In New York, there are thousands of stories like David's now, but only one of Paul's.

Like you, I recall the most mundane details of that morning. As usual, Paul had to be at Shiso by 10 a.m., to do prep for the midtown lunch rush. But he'd decided to drive, in order to swing by one of my clients after work; a two-year-old Basenji had suddenly started peeing everywhere, and I'd agreed to take the dog in for retraining.

Though Paul made twice as much as a chef as I did as a part-time dog trainer, he always put our work on a par. So he left that morning at about quarter to nine, in time to stop by the pet store on Broadway for more dog treats and kibble. He called me a few minutes later, on his way into the store, because on the car radio he'd heard about the "accident" at the North Tower. We worried about David, uncertain which tower he worked in, while I hurried to switch on the TV. That was the last time we spoke. I forgot to say "I love you." We didn't say that all the time. We didn't want it to get tired.

I tried calling you, Sarah, but of course the line was busy. Then the second plane hit, and that's when the horrible realization bloomed for us all: that the first plane hadn't been an accident, either.

I've reconstructed the rest of the timeline thanks to the Harrisons, about whose circumstances I now know more than I wish. I've finally lost touch with that couple, though they were almost torturously attentive for a while.

Along with their three kids, Joy and Buddy Harrison had gotten an early start after a long weekend upstate, at a lakeside resort they could only afford with post-Labor Day, off-season rates. The day before, they'd shopped at discount outlets to stock up on sports socks, underwear, and family packs of chicken; with luggage as well, their rattletrap minivan was crammed. Around 9:30, they'd been inching down Riverside Drive, listening to the radio like everyone else. Traffic had been bad, and Buddy would be late for work, the kids late for school; no one had yet entered the universe where there was no work, there was no school. The news was distracting, upsetting, so it took them a few minutes to notice that their engine was on fire.

The Harrisons parked at a cockeyed angle at 79th Street, and at least had the wit to drag their kids out before going after the economy-pack toilet roll. Buddy tried calling for the fire department, but 9-1-1 – the number didn't yet seem eerie – was no longer answering.

Driving down Riverside to work, Paul would have spotted a minivan by the side of the road with flames licking from under the chassis. He was the only motorist to pull over; by then, everyone else was already paranoid and doubtless assumed the van was a car bomb. The Harrisons are fiercely budget-minded, and even my beguiling husband couldn't get them to write off hundreds of dollars' worth of discount products. So Paul helped them drag their booty onto the sidewalk, while the fire got worse. Minding the kids, Joy Harrison sidled over to our Volvo, whose radio was still playing. That's when they announced that the Pentagon had been hit. Joy gasped, Buddy rushed over, and they listened for a moment.

Paul was still in their backseat. He must have been overcome with smoke. And then the minivan erupted.

I'll take their word for it that Buddy and Joy "streaked" to their van to pull my husband from the flames, but by then Paul was badly burned. They tried calling an ambulance, but 9-1-1 was still jammed. Ironically, they could hear a cavalcade of ambulances wailing down the West Side Highway the whole time, only a hundred feet away, but the emergency vehicles were all headed downtown, not to some lowly car fire on Riverside and W. 79th.

This must have been right around the time you called me, Sarah. You were feeling so helpless, unable to reach David's cell; the satellite networks were overloaded. We both gawked at CNN, frightened personally of course, but frightened also in a larger way that was unfamiliar. During one of our gaping silences, the South Tower emitted a great grey plume on-screen and disappeared into smoke, like a quarter-mile-high magic trick. We inhaled together. We held our breaths together. We screamed together. Sharing that moment cemented our friendship for life. I don't regret that.

Meanwhile, I'm told, Buddy Harrison finally carried Paul to our Volvo to drive their rescuer to St Luke's himself. But by then traffic was hardly moving, and they must have lost a lot more time sitting in it.

The hospital called me at 11:30 a.m. They may have tried to get through earlier, but I'd been on the phone with my mother, who couldn't stop weeping.

"I don't understand," I said numbly to reception. "My husband had no reason to go downtown."

Then a doctor got on the line. This was unusually personable service, but you remember – every doctor, nurse, and paramedic was on call, poised, at every hospital in the city, and there was nothing for them to do. Nothing. A least Paul Eisenberg's peculiar misfortune provided busywork.

"Ms. Eisenberg, I should clarify," said the internist, and then he delivered the verdict that would cordon me off forever, that would exile me in a small, tinny, unimportant world, a tiny, private, incidental world, while the rest of the country lived in the tumult of history, of shifting tectonic allegiances, of wars and counterinsurgencies; of great moral choices, grand speeches, and noble sacrifices: "as far as we can tell, your husband's death had nothing to do with the World Trade Center."

In New York City, 148 people die every day – from strokes, traffic accidents, overdoses, or misguided acts of altruism. Ten years ago, my husband was one of them. But because he merely died *on* 9/11, I've been banished from the commemorations to which you've been invited for ten years.

Paul didn't burn himself in Shiso's kitchen, so I've received no survivor's benefits from Worker's Comp. While still childless, Paul and I had seen no reason to carry life insurance. Without a second income, I've had to give up the Upper West Side apartment. I sold most of our furniture. I'm stuck in a walk-up in Queens. Where the supermarket signs are all in Chinese. I can't even afford cable.

So you can imagine it was difficult for me when that Victims Compensation Fund awarded you *2.2 million dollars*. Lump sum, tax free. And you still objected it wasn't enough. It didn't reflect David's lifetime earning power. But Sarah, I lost my husband too. Yet no one's given me a dime, and I still pay taxes on every minimum-wage dog-walking check. That's right, I've been reduced to dog-*walking*.

Everyone who died *in* 9/11 is described as "a hero." If you don't mind, David did nothing but go to work. On his own initiative, Paul was helping a family in distress. Paul was a hero. David was a casualty. Yet David's picture was in the paper, not my husband's. David's passing is mourned annually by millions of people, but no one besides immediate family remembers Paul's.

You've always emphasized how losing David was especially terrible because you have kids. Doesn't that make you lucky? You've preserved your husband's very DNA. I have nothing to show for Paul. Some days I can't even remember what he looked like, while your children's faces remind you daily of David's. Remember, Paul and I had just started to try – and I cried myself sick near the end of that September when I got my period after all.

You've been envious that I had a body to bury. Well, don't be. I may have taken possession of an incinerated corpse, but that body has never kissed me goodnight, or promised to pick up kibble on the way to work. It hasn't proved good for much.

You've sometimes strained to include me. True, were the first responders not all streaming downtown – where they would line up, bumper-to-bumper, pointlessly empty – maybe Paul could have gotten to the hospital in time to save his life. Maybe if the Pentagon hadn't just been attacked, the Harrisons would have been more attentive, and dragged my husband to safety. Still, I'm not officially a "9/11 widow," and I've never claimed to be.

In some ways, that cataclysm has been the making of you. Before, you didn't even have a job, and now you give speeches at fund-raising lunches. You delivered a statement to the 9/11 Commission. You get letters published in the *New York Times*, which gives you special credence because of your bona fides. You attend the commemoration every year in smart black suits. You seem to know who you are now, while your children wear their heritage with pride: their father died *in 9/11*.

You have fierce political opinions, where before they were hazy – which has sometimes put us at loggerheads. I pointed out that the Park51 mosque is planned *near* Ground Zero, not *at* Ground Zero – and I of all people should understand the importance of prepositions. You were offended. The mosque was "insensitive," you said. But we can't ban a particular religion from a whole area of New York, I said, it's unconstitutional. You just kept repeating that word, *insensitive*. I got the message. My opinion didn't count. Your opinion was privileged.

Sarah, maybe that's what I am trying to say: I know it doesn't seem that way, but you *are* privileged. Around the world, over 150,000 people die every day – from cholera, dysentery, cancer, starvation, war, or sheer neglect. Almost none of their families enjoy the widespread sympathy of total strangers that yours does. David's death means something – not only to you and your kids, but to the city, the country, the world – while all I can construe from the debacle on Riverside Drive was that my husband was a nice guy. The rest of us suffer our losses as deeply as you do, but can make nothing of them. We're left with no large, dark force like "Islamic terrorism" to locate at their heart, just an ongoing void and inexplicable awfulness. We anguish alone and in silence. Our anniversaries are quiet, dolorous affairs, and the company with whom we share them dwindles.

In primary school, a *preposition* was "anything an airplane can do to a cloud." Since flying objects can apparently go *through* and even *out* the other side of tall buildings, perhaps a preposition is now "anything an airplane can do to the World Trade Center." Whatever their definition, prepositions are powerful words. *At* Ground Zero, *near* Ground Zero. *In* 9/11, *on* 9/11. Our diverging fates have hinged on one letter. This year, perhaps you can finally afford some backhanded gratitude for that small "i."

Your life was shattered on an iconic shorthand, "9/11"; mine fell apart on plain old September 11th, 2001. Your loss has filled you, made you greater, connected you to your neighbors and your country, and raised you to a select elite. My loss has diminished me, as losses diminish most people. I will still join you in spirit downtown this September, and I, too, will sorrow that night as twin spotlights shoot, bend, and evanesce into the sky. But spare a thought for us exiles – the bereaved for no grand reason. Your lot has been hard. But I believe my lot has been even harder. For a decade, the conceit of our friendship has been quite the reverse.

Still with great affection,
Rachel

LIONEL SHRIVER IS THE AUTHOR OF TEN NOVELS, INCLUDING THE *NEW YORK TIMES* BESTSELLERS *SO MUCH FOR THAT* (A FINALIST FOR THE 2010 NATIONAL BOOK AWARD) AND *THE POST-BIRTHDAY WORLD* (2007). WINNER OF THE 2005 ORANGE PRIZE, THE INTERNATIONAL BESTSELLER *WE NEED TO TALK ABOUT KEVIN* WAS ADAPTED FOR A FEATURE FILM BY LYNNE RAMSAY IN 2011. HER ELEVENTH NOVEL, *BIG BROTHER*, IS PUBLISHED IN 2013.

SPELLED BACKWARD

Emma Donoghue

Carly wasn't really one for travel. In her experience it often turned out to be about going a hell of a way for not that big of a hoopla.

Simon had been the same way till he'd caught the marathon bug, at forty-nine. The prospect of the big 5-0 (Hawaii Five-O, he called it) had scared the pants off him, so his once-weekly run was suddenly every other day, and the next thing Carly heard, he'd signed up for their local Half Marathon. And that was such a whoop-de-doo, apparently – she hadn't seen it, she'd had to work that weekend – that he'd immediately started training for the Chicago Full. Some of his runner buddies described it like religious conversion, but Simon made it sound more like the claw in that arcade game: just swung down one day, hooked him, that was that.

Rome would be his sixth marathon. Not a very dramatic number, but his first outside the States, and the timing was miraculous, because they were managing to stop off for the race on their way to a villa in a vineyard for their best friends' daughter's wedding. 'I can't believe you're going to see this one,' Simon said. 'Finally!'

'Me too,' she murmured, wrestling with the two-part hangers in the hotel's poky wardrobe. *Me neither?* Carly often wasn't a hundred per cent sure how to say things.

'According to the forums it's a fast course, avoids most of the hills, and the normal winning time's around two-oh-eight, though you have to be prepared for log jams in the first few turns. Sixteen thousand they're expecting, maybe nearer seventeen. Rome's on everyone's bucket list.'

'Guess it's the beauty,' she murmured. But she knew that was a mistake the minute it was out of her mouth.

'Beauty? It'll all go by in a blur, hon,' he said painedly. 'I'll be keeping my eyes on the three-forty-five pacesetter, he'll have a – is it red? I think it's red, I must check.'

'Don't worry, you'll check everything.' Though she was privately amused by the idea that Simon might confuse the colors and follow the wrong flag. A too slow one or a too fast one, which would be a greater disaster?

'There's a crucial moment, apparently, when you pass the Spanish Steps – this incredible staircase all down a hill, one of the poets died there,' Simon told her, 'and half the crowd starts rubbernecking, trying to take pics of themselves, but if you just look straight ahead and don't break an ankle on the cobblestones you can gain maybe thirty seconds.'

Carly kept nodding, as she slid dresses onto hangers. Marathoning was Simon's baby, so who was she to poke fun? Honolulu 2010, when he'd got up at three a.m. with about thirty thousand Japanese guys to start the race in the dark – he'd flown home and told everybody it was *life-altering*. Weird, to think of his life altering, while she'd been asleep.

He was carb loading today, which meant sprinting on the spot in the hotel room followed by gigantic cans of some formula that made him burp – from the fitness store back home, because *go with what you know*. Plus fiber tablets. 'Remember that photo of a winner with poop running down his legs?' Carly marveled.

'Well,' he said, 'sometimes there are lines for the porta-potties, and if you stand around even for a minute your muscles are going to seize up.'

'Simon. You would not.'

He shrugged, all battle-hardened.

'You're full of it.'

'As it were.' Smirking.

Simon had to go off by subway to the Marathon Village now, to show his medical cert and pick up his race package. 'There's a four k called RomaFun, for the families,' he mentioned.

'That's OK, hon. I'm fine just hanging.' Then she added, 'You've got seven years on me. I figure I can afford to loll around and eat gelato.'

'Seven years older but ten years fitter,' he said, like it was a joke, but not really.

Rome had six hundred churches, according to the guidebook. Carly didn't go into any as they gave her the heebie jeebies. At first it was nice just walking, drinking in the foreignness and all. It was a bit cold for gelato but she had some million-cal cake.

By the time her heels started hurting she was in a huge park, the Borghese something, littered with monuments; it was starting to rain and Simon, of course, had the umbrella. She ducked into a fancy schmancy white mansion that turned out to be a gallery, which was something Carly hadn't been in since high school.

'You're kidding me,' she told the woman behind the counter. 'I need a reservation to look at pictures?'

'We have some openings at five, *signora*, if you'd like to come back …'

'Forget it, I'm only here to get out of the rain.'

And then wished she hadn't said that, because the guy in line behind her looked down his long nose like she was some kind of idiot.

The rain was pelting down now. Carly considered the cafe, but she was still weighed down by the last cake.

A girl tapped her on the arm. 'They won't take back my ticket. You want it?'

'Sure.'

Carly handed over fifteen euros for it. Then noticed that the ticket said eight fifty, but at that point the girl was curled up by the coat check, flirting into her phone, and the one o'clock ticket holders were all being herded towards the turnstile.

The art was incredibly old and way out there. It was hard to take it all in because every surface was so shiny, marble encrusted with gold, like some three-year-old girl's idea of pretty: more is more. (Or the Kardashians: didn't they have one room where everything was checkered?) Big white statues that all seemed – according to the little plaques – to be of rape, which seemed a weird theme for a living room; one girl was actually turning into a tree to get away from the creep. Carly didn't look at the ceilings because they hurt her neck (still stiff from the plane), and she figured if any of the pictures up there were all that, someone would have stuck them in a frame. There was one statue that made her laugh out loud, a hermaphrodite: a girl, it looked like, holding up her skirt and staring down at the most enormous boner.

On the second floor her feet were really throbbing and there was nothing not-priceless to sit on. Since she hadn't been raised religious, it all struck her as repetitious (how many mother-and-baby pictures did these Borghese need?) as well as pervy: Venus, Mary Magdalene, any excuse for tits. Art was a cult with rules you were supposed to just know:

(A) glide past most of the pictures with a slightly sad expression,

(B) when you spotted one of those little cards with the lines that looked like WiFi but were to do with the headsets half the crowd were wearing, move in close,

(C) squint, bend, lean in near enough to read the plaque but not so near the guard would taser you,

(D) step back without bumping anyone, stare again, nod, and

(E) glide on with a now-I-understand-the-mysteries-of-the-universe look on your face.

Carly was wishing she'd sat the rain out in the cafe when she saw it. Huge: a dark room, a woman in a red dress holding a naked kid under the arms, some leathery hag looking on. The mom had the boy's foot on hers like she was teaching him to foxtrot but actually she was stepping on a snake, just behind its head, a goddamn snake; it was writhing and twisting itself into a better position to lash the kid. Jesus! The young woman in scarlet all calm with her lovely stretched neck like, *trust me, Mommy knows what you need*, and the boy – a toddler, practically – with his nose wrinkled up all nervous, *no like snakey*, and the old hag standing right there doing fuck all, muttering *it's going to end in tears*, her face like she'd been skinned, of course they didn't have sun block back then but still. Carly edged through the reverent viewers till she could read the card: *Madonna dei Palfrenieri, 1605*.

Madonna, that meant the Virgin Mary, she must be the girl in red, and she and the hag had those little silver UFO things over their heads that meant they were holy. But the boy was totally real, one hand flung out and one curled up. He glowed like he was made of butter. Not circumcised, by the way, that didn't seem very kosher; his thing was pointing right at the snake. No loincloth or whatever they used for a diaper back in the day. Carly supposed kids just went in the gutter back then, like in the Third World; the past was one big Third World.

'Caravaggio painted people *in extremis*,' a guide was murmuring to her group. *In extremis*, that had to mean like extreme sports. 'He seized them at moments when the ground shifted beneath their feet,' the guide almost whispered, 'moments of inspiration, betrayal, vocation – crucifixion of course – conversion … Think of his *St Paul* falling off his horse on the road to Damascus. The reason, of course, why one refers to a Damascene moment, a great turning point in one's life.'

Oh one did, did one? *Not on my planet, lady.*

Carly moved on, but three rooms later she realised she wasn't taking anything in, because she was still bothered by that snake picture. So she pushed against the human tide, ignoring the glares of the guards, till she found her way back to it. *Your gorgeous tits are hanging out,* she found herself telling the Madonna in the scarlet dress, *and don't you see you're freaking Baby Jesus out, stamping on that snake?*

In the gift shop Carly saw a book called *Rome Is Love Spelled Backward*. But wasn't *love* spelled backward *evil* spelled wrong, like Eminem said in the song?

She picked up random things like key rings and scarves and mouse pads with paintings on them, a necklace just like the girl in a painting with a unicorn was wearing, only not real rubies obviously. She tried to find a postcard of the hermaphrodite to amuse Simon – she thought she'd scribble *Keep it up!* on it – but no luck. There was a magnet with a severed head on it; what kind of person would want that on their refrigerator? The label on the back said it was another Caravaggio.

The catalogue said the snake in the Madonna picture meant the devil, but still. You just didn't put a kid's bare leg that close to a dangerous animal; it was common sense, even back in 1605. The leathery one turned out to be St. Anne, Jesus's grandmother, and the Palafrenieri were the Pope's grooms, who'd commissioned the thing but sold it off fast because Anne was their special lady and they were pissed at Caravaggio for making her look like something out of a horror movie. People were always pissed at him and vice versa; he once beat up a waiter in an argument over some artichokes. That made Carly cough with laughter. The guy liked to paint knives and dirty feet: trailer trash basically. The severed head on the magnet was Goliath but it was also Caravaggio's own face; he painted that one for the Pope as a way of saying sorry after wasting some other guy over a tennis match and for four years he never stopped running all across Italy to avoid the slammer; his pardon did finally turn up but by then he'd died of a fever.

The Borghese had six paintings of his altogether, Carly found out. She tried to go back in by the turnstile to see the others but the guard said her time slot was *finito*.

Taking a taxi to the hotel, she counted four different Irish pubs with gigantic signs: she'd forgotten it was St. Patrick's Day.

'Great free swag,' Simon crowed, showing off his red *Marathona Di Roma* t-shirt and matching backpack, 'and pretty good amenities en route, sponge stops, though the hydration stations are only every five k. I think I'm doing the right thing, bringing my own energy gels ...'

'I'm sure you are,' said Carly, rubbing peppermint lotion into her cramped soles.

They had dinner in an *osteria* that Simon's guidebook called *guaranteed untouristy*.

'But we are tourists,' she pointed out.

He made a face. 'When I travel for a marathon, I prefer to experience that place as it really is, you know, mile by mile, on my own two feet.'

Carly was tempted to say that it took a lot of planes and rental cars to schlep his two gnarly feet all over the world. Or that just about any place would be more itself on another day of the year, without sixteen thousand foreigners thumping through it. Much of the pleasure of marriage lay in mentally savoring the remarks you wouldn't let yourself make.

No question of wine the night before a race, even though it was St. Paddy's; she felt crass for having suggested it, like Simon was pregnant or something. He ordered the risotto with the fewest words and what sounded like some big chicken thing with roast potatoes. Carly pointed at random to *tagliatelle al ragu di lepre*, because it reminded her of Ragu sauces back home. 'Pasta with Leopard?' she wondered aloud, once the waiter had gone. 'Pasta with Lepers?'

That wrung a laugh from Simon, which wasn't always easy the night before a race. She made some casual reference to forty-two kilometers and he said 'Forty-two point one nine five.'

'Right,' she said, shutting her eyes so he wouldn't see her roll them.

They gossiped about the wedding party which was the original point of this trip. How had the girl they'd babysat so often – being kid-free themselves, they were always available – how had she managed to grow up and land herself an Italian TV star?

According to the latest family blog post, the father and mother of the bride were going to renew their vows right after the rehearsal dinner. 'What's that about?' Simon wondered. 'Has he had an affair?'

Over rock-hard *tartufo* he reminisced about his brushes with danger. 'Philly, last November: two DOA at the finish. Heart, of course. Twenty-one years old, one of those guys. The Greek who started it all, he delivered his message about the victory, then dropped down dead.'

'Are we still talking about Philly?'

Simon clicked his fingers beside her head as if to wake her up. 'Battle of Marathon, like eons B.C.'

What Carly would have liked to say was, *sorry if it's hard to believe you're going into mortal peril, hon, since you've done this five times already with nothing worse than a rash from your underwear elastic* …

But that really would be tempting Fate to strike Simon down tomorrow and leave her a widow at barely forty-six. Under the table, she knocked lightly on the faux wood.

To change the subject, she told him about the Caravaggio painting of the young mother in red. 'The books go on about him being way ahead of his time for his so-called realism, but I don't call it realistic to force a toddler to stamp on a snake with his bare foot …' She trailed off. 'What are you staring at me for?'

'You sound so angry.'

'I'm not angry, it's just a ridiculous painting.'

Simon's eyes lit up. 'This is about your brother.'

Carly felt rage like smoke rising from her head. 'What would make you – '

'That time you were minding him,' Simon butted in, 'and you didn't notice he'd been –'

'Didn't notice?' Her voice went way up and a woman at another table stared. 'Like I was watching TV and scarfing popcorn? I noticed all right, I noticed when he ran in screaming and sweating and puking and then went all floppy. I just didn't realise what it was that was doing it to him. I mean, forgive me if I wasn't telepathic. He didn't say where it hurt.'

'Carly –'

'The bite mark was under his freaking shorts, how was I to know to look under his shorts?'

'Nobody ever said it was your fault, hon. Did they?'

Her hand was locked around her fork.

'I blame your mom, if anyone, for leaving a teenager in charge of a two-year-old in a shack with no phone in the wilds of –'

'It was a bungalow,' Carly interrupted through her teeth. 'And we did own a phone, it'd just – the phone company had cut it off because of a mix-up.'

'OK.'

She made herself breathe out.

'Anyway, he was fine, when he came out of hospital,' Simon added.

He still was fine, her brother. Never quite achieved what they'd hoped for him, but hey, that couldn't be blamed on the rattlesnake.

So many little kids seemed special, but it was like it leaked out of them and they ended up ordinary adults.

The waiter threw a word over his shoulder. Carly smiled and nodded, and a few minutes later found that she'd accidentally ordered them espressos. Simon wouldn't risk it, but Carly tried hers: horribly bitter, though the flavor did kind of sing in her mouth.

Waiting for the bill, Simon finally figured out the dictionary on his phone, and told her that she'd just eaten hair.

'What?'

'*Ragout of hare*,' he read out. 'Like, long-eared rabbit.'

'No way,' cried Carly.

'How did it taste?'

'Great, actually.'

All the way back to the hotel, she could feel the hare, loping along inside her.

The big day: Carly woke with a crick in her neck, to a confusing soundtrack.

'Yeah, chances are still pretty good for a PB despite the jetlag and the wind factor. I'm a bit concerned about the uphill at forty k but at that point adrenalin should carry me ...' Simon, on the phone to his little sister. PB Carly knew: *personal best*, the invisible figure marathoners were always chasing through the streets. Some of the acronyms were harder. She only remembered LTS was *lactose-threshold speed* because when Simon had first explained it, she'd made some crack he didn't find funny about it meaning how fast he could run before he'd start leaking milk.

'No, they're not all one-fifty to one-seventy BPN, for me it's more a matter of mojo. "Born to Run", to start, obviously...'

His goddamn playlist.

'Then, let's see, I've got "I Ran" – the original, Flock of Seagulls, of course – "Can't Stop", "Till I Collapse", "Run to You", "Boom Boom Pow …"'

Carly burrowed under the pillow.

The hotel buffet was on the top floor, looking down on the blue-gray roofs of Rome. The oranges were the color of blood and the croissants had some kind of custard hidden inside. Simon would eat nothing but fruit, plus ginger capsules washed down with cups and cups of coffee to *clear himself out*. Would he do it, Carly wondered? If it came to it, would this man she called her husband really soil his pants for the sake of shaving a minute off his PB? Please, please not: time enough for that in thirty years when she was pushing his wheelchair.

The start line was right beside the Colosseum, which turned out to be way bigger and more broken than in the postcards. Simon kept adjusting the armholes of his garbage bag and issuing instructions. 'If you stand right there, by that – what is it, a cypress? – from, let's say twelve thirty, twelve twenty-five to be on the safe side, I figure you'll be able to get me crossing the line with the Colosseum right in the frame.'

He fiddled with the chip timer attached to his scarlet bib that said *Veterano 2*, meaning over fifty. 'Keep it set to video, remember, because I can always capture still shots from the footage.'

The volunteers were handing out water cups instead of bottles: 'Hey,' Simon muttered to himself, 'I guess that's why we travel, for things to be different.' He pulled a gel pack from the row in what Carly couldn't help thinking of as his ammo belt. 'Cocoa bean, how's that not chocolate?' he wondered, then emptied it in one long suck.

Men jogged by in ancient Roman gear with actual feathers coming out of their helmets. One was dressed as a Champagne bottle.

The crowd was thickening; an excitable woman in a silver mylar blanket almost knocked Carly over. Europeans just didn't have the same notions of personal space. She tried to imagine how bad the crowd would have smelled in Caravaggio's day. Oh my god, was that runner actually peeing on the Arch of Constantine?

'Eight forty-one. I'd better head into the corrals,' Simon announced, fiddling with his ear buds; 'the staggered starts can get kind of brutal.'

His Special Ops tone made Carly's lips purse: she just wished he'd admit that he loved every minute of this, even the waiting round with sixteen thousand other dorks in garbage bags.

She kissed him on the lips, as lovingly as she could manage. 'Oh, but –'

'What is it?' he demanded, already jogging on the spot.

Fine, if he was going to be like that, let him head off with her lipstick all over his mouth. 'Break a leg!'

He disappeared into the throng. And now Carly was meant to stand around for twenty minutes while the announcer screamed more and more shrilly over the PA, all for the unlikely chance that she'd be able to pick Simon out from the mass of runners taking off …

She turned on her heel.

Carly shopped a little – fuschia leather gloves for her mom, a dress with a huge fake fur collar for herself – and had a lukewarm *caffe latte*: she couldn't tell if this was how authentic Romans drank it, or if it was a matter of let's-treat-tourists-like-dirt.

She only went into the big white church of Sant'Agostino because there was a poster outside saying *Caravaggio*, with an arrow. It was spooky inside, with pictures and statues and tombs – lots of angels blowing trumpets – and how was she to know which was which? But finally she figured that there had to be a reason for a whole clump of tourists to be leaning over the gate of one little room. Joining them, she couldn't see a thing until somebody put a coin into a vending machine on the wall and a spotlight came on. Carly almost giggled: these priests were onto a good thing, selling light by the minute. A woman, the same hottie with the long neck as in the snake picture but looking tireder, standing with her legs crossed against a wall of flaking brick, clutching the same naked boy but with his sheet falling off, like he was going to slip out of her arms any minute. An old man and woman kneeling down, his big dirty feet practically sticking out of the painting. Then the light went off with a loud click.

The tourists shuffled and whispered. Carly, figuring most of them were students and broke, pushed over to the box and fed a euro in. She squeezed forward to the rail – she'd paid for the view, after all –

and read the English translation on the plaque, which said that the *Madonna di Loreto* was appearing as a statue come magically to life to these humble pilgrims and *gazing at them with gentle sympathy*. BS, thought Carly. More like a single mom saying *here, if you guys think the baby's some kind of god, you carry him for a while!*

'Lena was his girlfriend,' some kid said beside her.

Carly assumed they were talking about their high school till another boy said 'I read, his ho. He was a pimp actually.'

'But he was gay, you can't have a gay pimp.'

'Sure you can.'

Carly stared even harder at the girl in the picture, the real girl, whose neck must have killed her after long days of holding it in that position. Yeah, with that maroon velvet sleeve she did look a bit like she was on the game, like this was her regular corner but tonight she hadn't been able to find a sitter ...

The light went out again with a hollow snap. Carly moved away, past a couple scrutinising a marble column. 'The Caravaggio disease,' the Englishman murmured.

'Mm,' said his girlfriend, 'he attracts all the utter newbies.'

At the dimly lit book stall, Carly surprised herself by – perhaps to thumb her nose at the English couple? – shelling out forty-nine euros for Caravaggio's *Complete Works*. Softcover, but she could barely lift the thing.

'You have been to the Palazzo Barberini?' the old lady insisted on knowing.

'Ah, not yet.'

'You must go. Many Caravaggios.'

Picking her way across the cobblestones – some of them were so high and irregular, they were more like stepping stones – Carly toyed with a fantasy of just staying on. Not showing up at the finish line or at the hotel; never going home. Learning to like espresso. Letting Rome change her like Julia Roberts in what was that movie, or was it India?

At the Palazzo Barberini Carly shuffled through room after room, looking for that girl again, the long-necked Lena, but what suddenly seized her attention was a boy. A young man, really, but you could eat him with a spoon. The painting was like a playing card because the top and bottom reflected each other: the boy was kneeling down leaning over this big puddle or pool, staring hungrily at his reflection, or at least it had to be but it was darker so the white sleeve looked blue, like it was a different boy. His strong arms and back made the shape of a table, with his knee right in the middle forming a bright circle, the most undeniable knee Carly had ever seen: it punched out at her. He – the real boy – wanted to kiss his reflection, swallow it up – you could tell he'd never ever look away – but if he got any closer he'd fall in and shatter the image, or he might even drown, depending on how deep the water turned out to be.

Narciso, said the label, *Narcissus*. It was a Caravaggio; Carly felt a prickle of excitement that she'd spotted it, even if she was an *utter newbie*. Did his name mean *narcissist*, like, navel-gazer? She was dizzy now, falling into the dark center of the painting, wanting to touch that beautiful boy who was dead four hundred years and only made of paint anyway.

The thought struck her hard on the sternum: the joke was on her. This was a picture about pictures, or about whatever unreal mirror image you might fall for, lose yourself in. *Straighten up*, Carly told herself, *walk away, get on with your life while you still have it, that's what he's saying.* But she wanted to take this painting with her; wondered whether, if she lifted it off the wall, the guard had a hidden gun to take her down. Her pulse thundered in her throat. She had an uneasy feeling that she'd found her marathon. Her hook, her road to Damascus, her *boom boom pow*. The thing that was spelling her backward, the thing she was going to become a bore about, the thing for which there was at least an outside chance that she would be willing to poop her pants.

Her watch said twelve twenty-nine. She stared at it stupidly.

Pelting down the cobblestoned hill, *Complete Works* in its plastic bag banging her leg, Carly looked in all directions for a taxi. What would Simon say if she wasn't there at the finish line? She'd have to invent a minor traffic accident, a twisted ankle, and even then, would he find it in him to forgive her? She was out of breath already, which was ridiculous for a woman of forty-six, not even menopausal. Jealous, she suddenly registered that now with a sensation of sharp relief like the lifting of a scab: she'd been sick with jealousy because Simon had this thing. His body, his middle-aged and hardly-the-hottest body had run hundreds of miles and what about hers, what miraculous thing had Carly ever done with hers?

She found a cab at last; she didn't understand the driver's words but his sardonic tone was perfectly clear. When they'd had to take three rights in a row, she paid him and started off on foot again, past T-shirts that said *Veni Vidi Vici* or *All Roads Lead to Rome* or *Never Stop Running*, which made her think of Caravaggio but she pushed that away, clutched the wretched book to her stomach and ran faster, sliding on discarded trash bags and mylar blankets. Not checking the time, because what was the point, because she was late, late, too late. Past grinning, stumbling marathoners, with funny melted-looking medals round their necks. Some of them lying on the cobblestones stretching or ripping off their sneakers or their scarlet bibs, one on his knees puking – it was like the aftermath of an orgy – and a branch nearly took Carly's eye out; some crazy old lady was handing out actual tree branches with silvery leaves all over.

When her phone rang Carly leaped as if she'd been shot. She would just have to tell Simon she hadn't heard it, in all the noise of the crowd. *12:49*, the screen reproached her. Then a message popped up: *Retrieving bag then will wait left of trophy table. 3:46:29 beats Philly time. Good footage?*

Men and their fucking obsession with the finish, the money shot ... Carly rehearsed her story: some bystander had elbowed her away from the cypress tree at the crucial moment, before she could turn the camera on. Or should she toss the thing into the Tiber and claim some pickpocket had stolen it? Too complicated. As she ran she punched in *OMG did u here me sccream yr name?? 3:46 honey u made me soproud.*

It was actually true; through the guilt, she was feeling something for Simon that could only be described as love. She made it another hundred yards through the litter of ancient ruins that blocked her way to the Colosseum.

His next message was more clipped. *Where u? Need to keep mving or muscles stiffen.*

She stopped for a second to heave a breath. *Meet front door of Coloss*, she improvised.

That bought her a minute of running before the expected answer: *Wh is front, thing is holes all round like swiss cheese???*

Forget Coloss, standng right in mid of big arch, she sent back, figuring that by the time he squeezed his way through the sweaty crowd it would be true, and if not she could always say she'd confused one gigantic arch covered in carvings of a massacre with another.

Gratitude, sudden gratitude for the real liveness of Simon, no matter how snippy he was going to be when she finally turned up. Gratitude for his beating red heart. She should be down on her knees thanking whoever that what her husband had discovered, at fifty, was marathoning rather than the predictable sportscar-and-bimbo combination. This might not be some fancy villa but she was renewing her vows in her own way: *I will show up in the end, I swear it.* Carly wouldn't be the nay-saying hag any more, she'd be Simon's trumpeting angel.

And if disaster came – no, more like when, time wounds all heels, wasn't that what they said? – when disaster came worming up Carly would stamp its fucking head off. The triumphal arch was so close now, a minute at most. For the rest of their lives she was going to be telling Simon – and telling others, in his hearing – what he'd looked like as he crossed the line: how she'd been so dumbstruck by the god she'd married that she'd forgotten to turn the camera on, would you believe it? And for all his eye-rolling and calling her an airhead, Simon would be secretly thrilled that *in extremis* Carly hadn't been able to take her eyes off his stern, sweat-washed face long enough to check the power button. In the end, she would almost believe that version herself, or at least picture it that way, a tiny image held forever in her mind's eye.

BORN IN DUBLIN IN 1969, EMMA DONOGHUE NOW LIVES IN CANADA AND HAS NEVER RUN A KILOMETRE IN HER LIFE. HER BOOKS INCLUDE THE BOOKER- AND ORANGE-SHORTLISTED *ROOM*, *SLAMMERKIN*, *THE SEALED LETTER* AND, MOST RECENTLY, *ASTRAY*.

WHINE AND CRUSHED ROSES

Will Self

I woke up on the morning I was to begin writing this essay and, as is my custom, put on the *Today Programme* on Radio 4. In times past I used to feel this geared me in, not only to the news cycle itself, but also to the select circle – 4,000? 14,000? 140,000? – of those in Britain who are directly driving the public policy agenda. But over the past year or two the pitch of the *Today* interviews seems to have risen, up and up, to the point where presenters and politicians alike all seem to speak with the Pinky and Perky voices of helium-inhalers. I don't fault the BBC for this – I think it more likely to be me. I am disengaged, I tell myself, my mind fixed on the lengthier time scale necessitated by the writing of long-form fiction; and so I shower, then plod damply downstairs to the kitchen, where I begin to make the children's breakfasts. But on this particular morning, still abed, I heard on *Today* that a report from the accountancy firm Wilkins Kennedy, purveyors of fiscal analysis by appointment to the markets, had revealed that in the last five years the rate of pensioners going into insolvency had increased by 111 percent, four times faster than the general population. Government policy – on interest rates, on the money supply itself – was directly responsible for this fact: that even those the welfare and dignity of whom the Coalition extolled above all others – the vulnerable elderly, who had put nest eggs aside – were nonetheless going bankrupt.

Then, on the evening I had finished writing this essay, I sat slumped on the sofa and remarked casually to my wife that I'd heard that George Osborne, the Chancellor of the Exchequer, had been fulsomely booed while handing out medals at the Paralympics. She confirmed that this was indeed so, and I asked: 'Was it just scattered catcalls?' And she replied: 'Oh no, it was the entire stadium.' A quick visit to YouTube confirmed that this was true: Osborne, his face shiny with embarrassment, stooped to loop a ribbon about a wheelchair-bound athlete, while a great groundswell of derision threatened to inundate him. But how could this be? I mean, the Paralympics are an unequivocally good thing, right? Some of us may have winced at the yea-saying coinage 'Jubilympics', but the successful Paralympics, surely, represented British values unsullied by mercantilism: tolerance, fairness, inclusiveness, and a preparedness to acknowledge that anyone, regardless of their physical attributes, can be a winner.

The difficulty for Osborne was that the massed crowds in the stadium were responding to a savage hypocrisy enshrined in the very ceremony they were witnessing. On the podium were the elite disabled the government would like us all to focus on; just as they would prefer us to concentrate on elite able athletes rather than school children deprived of sports facilities by their cuts, or our

Regal Pensioner figurehead rather than all the ordinary old folk who are going bust. However, in the stands were a lot of disabled people and their carers who understood only too well how punitive the government was being to those who are suffering from illness and disability. Newly leaked plans for £71 per week to be docked from those in receipt of the Employment and Support Allowance if they fail to take part in 'work-related activities' (often unpaid placements) were only the latest indignity to be heaped onto the disabled, who are also now subject to controversial 'health assessments' by the private contractor Atos, just another of the large corporates who doubtless hoped to improve their chances of securing further public money by sponsoring these selfsame Games.

Listening to the angry lowing of the crowd I felt relieved: at last the summer circus was beginning to pall and people were waking up to the cold winter that was nigh, one without any accompanying bread. But this was no true politicisation, one that might be transferred via a collective understanding into concerted action, but rather an expression of a kind of mental diplopia: we are beginning to understand that things have gone drastically wrong but we lack the depth of vision to conceive of how to put them right. There are myriad parties to our self-deception, and us writers are by no means the worst of them, but we're culpable as well. Of course we are.

I remember reading an interview with Martin Amis sometime during the dying days of John Major's Conservative government. 'We're all Labour now,' Amis said. It was a curious utterance; at once a transparently declarative statement – Amis, that personification of British middle-class *bien pensants*, responding to the Zeitgeist on its collective behalf – and a muddily gnomic one. After all, broken down into its constituent parts, and with the benefit of almost twenty years hindsight, Amis's slightly throwaway remark – knowing him personally, I can well imagine the sneering, two-tone twist he would've given to 'na-oww' – has acquired an unsettling force.

Here's my 2012 analysis: (1) *We're all* – This does indeed speak for a collective, although not simply one comprising the university-educated and liberally inclined who happen to be cultural producers: artists, writers, media functionaries and so forth. Given the curious synergy between the expansion of tertiary education throughout the Blair years and the infiltration of the web into every cranny of the collective psyche, the numbers of people who qualify for Amis's 'We're all' is concomitantly far larger: a *lumpen bourgeoisie* whose very Catholicism – of taste, of lifestyle, of consumption, of informed opinion bedizening message boards – is nonetheless its defining feature. (2) *Labour* – How prescient of Amis to have noticed by the mid 1990s the totalising capabilities of still-inchoate Blairism. That the parliamentary party had long since ceased to conform to any remotely leftist agenda was a given. After all, in *The Road to Wigan Pier* (1936), George Orwell was already writing dismissively of 'Labour Party backstairs-crawlers' as among socialism's principal enemies. But the very connective between the universal quantifier 'all' and the particular designator

'Labour', now seems to me to be the very hypoteneuse of the triangulation Blair effected on party policy, shifting it steadily to the centre ground, even as that centre was itself sliding inexorably and tectonically rightwards. (3) *Now* – Without resorting to the high-flown dialectics of cultural theorists in the mould of Fredric Jameson or Slavoj Žižek, it still seems to me that Amis had the particular character of our era, namely it's omnivorous contemporaneity, locked down tight with his ironic 'now'. Our go-round takes place within a rapidly accelerating feedback loop of cultural ephemera and political minutiae in which we can go from one year to the next without seeing any object, phenomenon or process that has not been either summoned into existence or crucially influenced by humankind. The Amis-ian 'now' thus means 'forever' and is a key component in our inability to find a way out of this cul-de-sac.

We're all Labour now – and none more Labour, of course, than the Tories, who are fully paid-up subscribers to all the key modalities of Blairism: a preoccupation with presentation that, stretched like camouflage, conceals a truly substantive ideological core. I don't much believe in the power of national governments to fundamentally alter the course of national destinies, but if the British ones of the past three decades have achieved any traction on the canal boat that's MV *Britain*, they have at least all been pulling in the same direction – and more or less in lockstep. It's been a mistake on the left – to which I still adhere, emotionally if not practically ('We're all Labour now') – to cast Margaret

Thatcher as the villain of the piece; the only begetter of the Corbys and Kilbrides and Telfords full of multi-generational unemployed and rack-rented former council housing stock. But in fact, in terms of the neoliberal ideology, Thatcher was the Lenin to Blair's Stalin – she only launched the revolution with a ragbag of mutually contradictory ideas tempered by opportunism. It was left to John Major to bicycle spinsterishly about the fictitious village green her governments had laid down on the toxified post-industrial landscape for seven long and biblical years before the True Saviour arrived.

Justice and liberty, these were the watchwords for George Orwell when it came to a socialism that he believed capable of winning the assent of a majority of the British population. Writing *The Road to Wigan Pier*, he opposed such a socialism to the fascist storm clouds he saw gathering – clouds from out of which the Nazis' blitzkrieg would, in due course, strike. It took that Gotterdammerung to secure assent to social and economic justice in this country, but the achievements of the post-war Atlee administration, and the successive Tory governments that also subscribed to the Butskellite consensus, have been systematically dismantled since May 1979. The gulf between rich and poor in this country has been steadily widening now for many years. Disregard all the guff you may've read about the public sector – as a percentage of gross domestic product (GDP) our spending on the public sector is already the lowest in Europe, and if this tendency continues we will be spending less than the US by 2015. Despite all the efforts of the recent New Labour governments to end child poverty – remember them? – Britain still has the highest proportion of these waifs in the EU; and the clincher, the Trussell Trust, which supplies food aid to needy Britons, handed out food parcels to over 100,000 people last year – they are opening two new food banks every week, and state that if current trends persist half a million of your fellow citizens will be in need of their service by 2016.

It's against this backdrop that the strength of our political commitments needs to be judged. And when I say 'our' I mean the same plural pronoun identified by Amis. I grew up in the 1960s and 70s when it was assumed that writers were political animals. The declivities between right and left were seen as fissures that ran back in time to merge with the larger fault-lines of the interwar period. The Angry Young Men of the 1950s were roused by the hypocrisies and injustices that they saw around them, and while many of them subsequently leapt from left to right across the ideological crevasse, their howling crossed the void with them.

Go back further, to Cyril Connolly's *Horizon* in the 1940s, or before that to the agonies of the Spanish Civil War and the Popular Front against fascism, and you begin to partake of the visceral intensity that informs every line of Orwell's diatribe against a social system and political order that tolerated 6 million people living in poverty. But, in his lucid and penetrating survey of contemporary British poverty, *The Road to Wigan Pier Revisited*, Stephen Armstrong quotes Sarah Dransfield of Oxfam GB, who catalogues the conditions of exploited migrant workers and those in the construction industry where – as in the mines of the 1930s – health and safety guidelines are flouted, before concluding that just as Orwell wrote about the hidden people in poverty – those who are working, but not receiving a living wage – so 'Over six million people in the UK (today) are living in poverty and are working.' It is only when these travailing poor become egregious – sleeping, say, under central London bridges on the eve of the Queen's Diamond Jubilee, that anyone much asks: what is to be done? And soon enough this query floats up into the ether to join all the other electronic scrim of unanswerable commentary. But *plus ça change* – here's Jack London, witnessing a poor old street sleeper in the aftermath of Edward VII's 1902 coronation:

> This was the most striking thing, the general heartlessness exhibited on every hand. It is a commonplace, the homeless on the benches, the poor miserable folk who may be teased and are harmless. Fifty thousand people must have passed the bench while I sat upon it, and not one, on such a jubilee occasion as the crowning of the King, felt his heart-strings touched sufficiently to come up and say to the woman: 'Here's sixpence; go and get a bed.' But the women, especially the young women, made witty remarks upon the woman nodding, and invariably set their companions laughing.

London's *People of the Abyss* – which Orwell leant on heavily for his own *Down and Out in Paris and London* – was written at a time when the crossover between fictional creation and realistic summation was a given; the popular novelists of the era, such as H.G. Wells and Arnold Bennett, while opposed politically, nonetheless viewed questions of justice and liberty as intrinsic to their metier. I light upon novelists for obvious reasons. With the late Victorian and Edwardian dramatists the contrast is even more glaring between the ostensibly politicised – yet curiously value-neutral – docudramas of someone like David Hare, and the insistently and morally influential works of George Bernard Shaw. Who can imagine a rarefied contemporary aesthete writing this:

> Socialism, Communism, or whatever one chooses to call it, by converting private property into public wealth, and substituting co-operation for competition, will restore society to its proper condition of a thoroughly healthy organism, and insure the material well-being of each member of the community. It will, in fact, give Life its proper basis and its proper environment.

– as Oscar Wilde did in *The Soul of Man under Socialism* (1891), his Kropotkin-influenced anarchist diatribe. During the same period, you have the spectacle of political propagandists turning to fiction in order to advance their views – the second bestselling novel of the nineteenth century was Edward Bellamy's *Looking Backward* (1887), another third-way attempt to steer a course between the whirlpools of capitalist exploitation and socialistic expropriation. Bellamy's novel was so influential that it gave rise to an entire political party in the States, while in Britain William Morris was moved to write a fictive rejoinder, *News from Nowhere* (1890), that set out the case for his own brand of idealised Arts & Crafts communism. Neither of these novels was – or is – much good in literary terms, but that's beside the point; which is that a disjunction has taken place between the role of the writer of fiction, and that of the politically engaged writer. We look now in vain for the novel that will galvanise a torpid and corn-syrup-bloated readership into political solidarity.

It is not without cause that the supposedly saintly George Orwell is so often cited as the patron of both the British right and left, for he stands as perhaps the last public intellectual in this country to combine serious fiction with strong political commitment. His co-option by the right is a species of what the French Marxist Situationists termed '*détournement*' – the redirection or subversion of a message so that it can be used for the opposite of its intended end. This shouldn't surprise us: we live in a society and a political culture where *détournement* is the dominant form of discourse, the paradigm being an advertising industry that tirelessly pushes product into our crowded minds by packaging it in ironic deprecation. But we still buy it, because we're all Labour now, and our very sense of security in this identification means that we're 'liberated' to buy the latest nugget of micro-circuitry to be assembled in the sweatshops of the Pearl River delta.

When I cite Orwell as the last public intellectual to combine serious fiction with strong political commitment I refer specifically to his activism – when it comes to being active, you cannot beat picking up a gun and firing it at fascists; tramping along rain-dank streets bellowing 'Who let the dogs out, Bush! Blair!' doesn't come close.

If that broad swathe of the British populace that Orwell identified as ready and willing to accede to the just nature of socialism – if only it could be presented to them in the right, commonsensical way, freed from the alienating jargon of the Marxists and purged of the cant spewed out by sandal-wearing cranks – still exists (and of course it does, recall: we're all Labour now), then at least part of the failure of the left since the onset of the financial crisis in 2007–8 must be explained by this queer development: the British left have in recent years expanded their zone of operations to include not only the benighted Africans now extant, but even those long dead. The former inclination resulted in such 'campaigns' as Make Poverty History and Dump the Debt, objects that were as impossible to achieve as they were to gainsay, so that in even aspiring to them many young, idealistic and socially concerned people were simultaneously roused and rendered inert.

Foreign charity and identity politics have splintered the natural constituency of the left into groupuscules competing for conscience money alone; while the headline campaigns favoured by arty celebrities – against the persecution of Aung San Suu Kyi, or latterly Ai Weiwei – safely export their radicalism to territories where it has little if any traction. The colonisation of the past itself as an area fit for liberal *mea culpas*, is, I think, a direct result of the violent sundering of the left as its very crotch descended on the vaulting horse of the post-9/11 'interventions'. We're all Labour now, and none it seems were more Labour than the shareholders of Halliburton and their Neocon spokespeople, who aimed to export democracy through the barrel of artillery pieces firing depleted uranium shells into the shattered suburbs of Fallujah. The hijacking of internationalism – the traditional province of the left – by the interests of global capital, has been as perplexing to the ordinary, decent folk beloved of Orwell, as has been their bamboozling by the ineluctable inflow of low-paid foreign workers to Britain. Should these people be welcomed as poor, huddled masses yearning to be free, who will simply set the capstone on our own much-loved tolerance? Or rejected, as proof positive of the peonage implicit in globalised capitalism, an economic system that wrings from the burnt-out shells of nation-states the only comparative advantage they have left to offer: that of their own natives' impoverishment?

It's been nigh on a lustrum since the British taxpayer was compelled to shore up the balance sheets – and by extension the shareholders' portfolios – of the UK banks, but we've seen no renaissance on the left, no burgeoning of creative energy, no ideological innovation. How could there be such a phenomenon? Because we're all Labour now anyway, and being Labour means that what we're preoccupied by is a Big Endian–Little Endian battle over the reduction in the egg deficit, even as its yolk is draining away into the gutter. The late Christopher Hitchens, whose commitment to being oppositional cannot be gainsaid (and who, of course, appropriated Orwell for his own personal pantheon), was interviewed by Alex Linklater of *Prospect* magazine at his Washington apartment in 2008. In the course of a typically garrulo-bibulous encounter, Hitchens was driven to explain how it was that, despite his own apparent *détournements* he had, in point of fact, been on the right moral side of every political declivity that had opened up in the four decades of his writing and activism.

He may find himself on the other side of that grotesque oxymoron, the 'peace wall' that sunders Israel-Palestine, but in his own commentary on the momentous events of last year (*The Year of Dreaming Dangerously*, Verso), Žižek – who is pictured on the cover in a posture of unimpeachable radical chic, hands stuffed in jeans pockets, white T-shirted against a backdrop of a burning car and masked rioters – also indulges in the most shameless contortionism as he struggles to join the irreconcilably multidimensional dots between the several rebellions of the Arab Spring, the British student fees protesters, the Greek EU payback refuseniks and the Occupy rabblement. But at least Hitchens was – and Žižek is – a tryer. With the silence of the novelists a given, the political stage is left vacant for the antics of such poseurs as Julian Assange and George Galloway.

Last year, during the Occupy protests in London, a young friend got in touch with me to ask if I would go along to the free university the protesters had established and give a couple of lectures. I prevaricated: I had been along to St Paul's and seen the pathetic huddle of tents and the tatterdemalion flyers pasted on the surrounding walls. I had been struck by how unanchored it all felt: little nylon bubbles of the way we were, floating away from the surly gravity of the body politic. This looked like Greenham Common in the early 1980s but much, much diminished. What would be the point in squatting on the carpet tiling in order to preach to the converted; or, worse, act as a pedagogue to middle-class kids who were probably already neglecting their studies?

I regret this attitude now: something is always better than nothing, and while I may have thought this was taking a more deeply principled stand, the truth is I was simply sitting it out. We're all Labour now – and none of us are more Labour than the literary producers. The most pernicious paradox of contemporary Britain – one that Orwell, dying as he did in 1950, didn't live to see – has been the trade-off between his beloved liberty and his equally desired justice. It seems scarcely credible that we can have a society as free as our own, where a great diversity of behaviour is not merely tolerated but permitted, and yet still find ourselves the passive accessories to an unjust system.

Put bluntly: while we're twittering (or, more precisely, Tweeting), the vultures are circling then gliding down to feast on the available carrion. It might be argued that in this strange new environment of ebooks and devices there is no way for any single writer to come up with a 'big idea' any more than he or she could claim that much of that many people's already frayed attention. But I don't believe the problem is essentially conceptual – rather, I think it relates to

the economic basis of literary creation. Writers who are serious –
and by this I mean writers who write from a sense of needing to
express something, rather than simply manufacturing a product
aimed at a given demographic – are nonetheless subject to the
same market forces as any other sole traders who are also primary
producers. But unlike dairy farmers, or miners in the Forest of
Dean, our primary product is not scaled: some words are worth far
more than others.

There is no real fraternity among writers, no trade union to
speak of – it is left to the monarchy, in the shape of the Royal
Literary Fund, to provide hand-outs to ageing and economically
inutile writers. The literary earnings pyramid is, at its peak, as
acuminate as the Shard – and at its base as wide as Cheops. In
this situation, with increasing numbers of producers clamouring
for a declining share of a collective attention span that is itself
being progressively and electronically whittled away, it can be no
surprise that there is little appetite for equality in the republic of
letters: poor writers – like the benighted of that other republic,
America – are fervent believers in the dream of striking it rich;
while those of us who are earning well protect our word horde as
jealously as any prospector in the Klondike guards his grubstake.
Of course, this doesn't prevent any of us from expressing the
wildest of revolutionary aspirations: To the barricades! Off with
their heads! Eat the rich! Turn the bankers on the rotisseries of
their favourite restaurants! But such sentiments are only another
morsel to be pondered over at the great smorgasbord of available

tastes – they need not be taken too seriously; after all, we're all Labour now – and even if some of us are too exhausted, too ill-fed and too ill to properly comprehend where their next literary meal is coming from, we can rely on the charity shops to dole them out parcels of our leftover words.

But words simply won't cut it in the current situation. Like Orwell, who I reclaim here and now for the left, it is time writers resorted to deeds.

WILL SELF IS THE AUTHOR OF EIGHT NOVELS, FIVE COLLECTIONS OF SHORT STORIES, THREE NOVELLAS AND SIX NON-FICTION WORKS. AS A JOURNALIST AND ESSAYIST HE HAS CONTRIBUTED TO A PLETHORA OF PUBLICATIONS OVER THE YEARS, AND HE IS A REGULAR BROADCASTER ON RADIO AND TELEVISION.

ENCOUNTER WITH A STRANGER

Cecelia Ahern

When I was sixteen years old, a woman sat next to me on a park bench. She was visibly upset, seemed fragile, her hands trembled as she buttoned up her coat to protect herself from the bitter harsh cold. She sniffled a few times, her nose filled from a recent bout of tears. The tip of her nose was red, like a garden gnome's, her face make-up free, her skin raw, her blemishes revealed to the world. Her eyelashes were barely visible under her eyelids, which were swollen like sponges holding too much water and beneath which hid two small beady blue eyes. Sadness seemed to have sapped the life from her, she was so filled to the brim with sorrow, like a sponge, she was sure to begin seeping.

I watched her from the corner of my eye, wondering whether she would speak or not, wondering whether I should. There was an atmosphere. Not the usual one around strangers, not an awkward one. Not as though we shared an elevator and were holding our breaths in the unusual suspended time that elevators bring. No; it wasn't the same. An elevator carries the sound of two people not saying anything. This moment with the stranger had the sound a person makes *before* they say something, that intake of breath, the look on our face before the words come tumbling out. She looked ready, I felt ready, but the words never came.

Eventually I settled into her company and my alert antenna went down. I disappeared into my head, half-thinking of what I'd wear out later that night, the other half watching the little girl I was baby-sitting playing on the swings, legs kicking back and forth, arms up and hands and fingers stretched as they tried to reach the sky. I thought of Adam, the boy I fancied, the boy who made my heart beat wildly. I'd met him at a house party a few weeks ago but I'd seen him around the neighbourhood months before. He was two years older than me, ahead of me in school, and I could just never find a way to talk to him. I couldn't find the words, couldn't find a topic, couldn't find the courage. He made me react in a way that I'd never experienced before; when I saw him he sent my heart racing, and when he looked at me he made me feel self-concious, as if every tiny little move I made was awkward and unnatural. I had to think about what I was doing, concentrate on getting it right. Even if it was merely walking by him, I had to focus on putting one foot in front of the other. He played havoc with all my internal wiring. He'd finally asked me out, his parents were away and he was having a house party, and so that night would be our first night together. I'd had butterflies in my stomach all week just thinking about it. The lady broke into my thoughts, reminding me she was there.

'Listen to me,' she said, with an urgency in her voice. Her fingers gripped my arm, I felt her nails through my rain jacket.

And I listened. She talked about choices, about the importance of making the right ones, about stepping back and seeing things from afar. Like I was doing today, at the park. Do that with everything she told me. When you're in the middle of it all, you don't see it too well, it's a spin, she said.

She kept her hand wrapped around my arm, clinging to me as though I was going to run any moment. The tighter she grabbed, the more I wanted to run. But I didn't. Something about her made me stay. Some of what she said went into my head, other parts were lost as I tried to figure out the moment.

And then she was gone. As quickly as she'd appeared. Her words of advice like a parcel of her experience wrapped in a big red bow had been delivered and deposited by my feet, the packaging and paper were left strewn about the bench.

I told a few people about her that day, particularly at the party when I ran out of other things to say, and she eventually turned into a joke, an odd crazy woman in a trench coat who grabbed my arm and ranted about decisions and choices. But as I grew older I thought about her and her words, realised there was some sense in those that I could recall.

Thirty years on from being the young girl on that bench, I dressed to go out in the cold and looked in the mirror at my tear-stained middle-aged face. At my wits' end, no time for make-up, I threw on a trench coat and ran. On the way down the stairs, tears blinding my steps, I stumbled and almost fell but a hand reached out and caught me. A peaceful elderly woman with a gentle smile, pitying eyes that sparkled so blue I froze and got lost in them momentarily. She handed me a tissue which I accepted gratefully and found a quiet place outside to hide and blow my nose and wipe my tears.

Walking in the park, I saw a girl, sixteen years old, looking across at the playground with youth, vitality and hope written across her face. Trembling, I sat next to her and buttoned up my coat, trying to think of the right words to teach her about what would come. They came out, tumbled out really all a jumble, I couldn't quite form them as I hoped. But I tried my best. She stayed thankfully, but I could see that a part of her wanted to leave. The most important part of her stayed. I did my best to stop it from happening again, the hurt over and over again.

When I was sixteen, a woman came and sat next to me on a bench. That woman was me. She told me to listen and I didn't. But I hear her now.

When I was eighty years old, I stopped a woman from falling on the stairs, I gave her a tissue and didn't bother with words; it would all right itself in the end.

CECELIA AHERN HAS WRITTEN FOR TELEVISION AND STAGE AND IS THE AUTHOR OF NINE NOVELS INCLUDING *PS, I LOVE YOU*, WHICH BECAME A BOX-OFFICE HIT STARRING HILARY SWANK. HER NOVELS ARE PUBLISHED IN OVER FORTY LANGUAGES.

THE HEADSHOT

David Harsent

A cool, clear morning rain-washed by last night's storm …
  First light
came in with a long, thin line of pearl above a long, thin line
of unsmudged aquamarine and he sat just fine in the crosshairs,
  sat just right

for a headshot, still as you like, as if he were thinking something
  through
as if he were tight on a recollection, say, of having slept alone
for more than a year, then woken to find her at the door, and that
  the true

moment of turning, the moment when things came good for
  a time.
A hawk dropped into the gunsight, a long way back but seeming
  to lean
on the wind just a handspan off from where he sat. As it started
  to climb

he made a slight movement, not to get up, more to shift his
    weight,
but soon settled back, still caught full-on. His face seemed to
    burn
in the dark frame of the roundel, held on a single breath, on a
    single thought:

the way she stepped in as if to stay, what she brought with her
    from the other life –
who knows? – but something that made him suddenly quicken
    and turn
to look straight down the barrel as if he might wave. As if he
    might wave and laugh.

DAVID HARSENT'S MOST RECENT COLLECTION, *NIGHT*, WAS TRIPLE SHORT-
LISTED IN THE UK (FORWARD, COSTA, T.S. ELIOT) AND WON THE GRIFFIN
INTERNATIONAL POETRY PRIZE. *IN SECRET*, HIS VERSIONS OF POEMS BY YANNIS
RITSOS, WAS PUBLISHED IN OCTOBER 2012.

RED PINS ON A MAP

Victoria Hislop

Heathrow Terminal 5. "Terminal" suggested an ending rather than a beginning, a place from which people left but never returned. This is how it seemed to Valerie Smith that morning. A venue for farewells.

In the centre of this vast and gleaming space, her teenaged son, bent double beneath a rucksack, fiddled with his mobile phone. Valerie looked at her watch and then glanced up at the board. From counting the weeks, days and hours until her boy's departure, she realised that it was now only a matter of minutes away. She cast a brief glance at him and then stooped to pick something up from the polished floor. His luggage tag already lay at his feet and she re-attached it, fastening it with a double-knot.

"James Smith." His handwriting still seemed so childlike, the simple, rounded letters almost unchanged since primary school days. She fought back her tears, busying herself with one of the backpack's zips that gaped open to reveal the contents: T-shirts, socks and an impractical, near-empty tube of toothpaste.

James was deep in conversation.

"Here? Where? Right. Right … OK. Yep. Yep …"

Valerie looked around at the other passengers in the terminal. Most people checking in were men in suits, some of them leaving small cases at the Bag Drop, but most of them breezing through with their executive brief cases.

They filed across the empty space like robots, calm, purposeful, focused, knowing to the last split second how many minutes they required for passport control, security and boarding.

Valerie knew that James's life in the next few months would be anything but micro-managed. This was his chance to amble freely round the world and visit places on a whim. Perhaps these self-assured men in suits had once travelled in jeans and a fleece, but she found it impossible to imagine James ever turning into one of them.

Oblivious to his mother's fiddling with tags and zips, James began to wander off. She saw where he was heading and then recognised a boy she had once met at school, another snail-like figure, carrying his worldly goods upon his back.

James reached out and took his friend's hand in a manly handshake.

Two adults stood behind the other boy. The woman was whimpering. In one hand she held what look like a table tennis ball, but was actually a tightly screwed up handkerchief. A few feet away, a tall, greying man stood looking distractedly in the other direction, away from his son and away from his wife.

The three adults seemed to circle the two boys, but they were already extraneous and the man moved around to introduce himself to Valerie.

"Hello, I'm David Hardingly, Ed's dad," he said.

"James's mum," she replied. "Valerie."

Both of them vaguely recognised each other from school events.

"Sorry. My wife's a bit upset. Ed hasn't really been away before."

"And he's your only one?"

"Yes. Same for you, isn't it?"

She nodded. She didn't really need a reminder. James's departure would leave her, for the first time in nearly nineteen years, entirely alone.

She was already bracing herself for her return home, knowing that the house would echo with its emptiness, but reflected that even this would be preferable to a home that rattled with the sobs of a hysterical woman. There was no other way to describe the state that Ed's mother was in. The boy did not even look embarrassed even though his mother's crying was probably audible at the other end of the terminal. She was howling, and every so often there was a high-pitched gasp, followed by a moaning exhalation of breath. Valerie flinched.

Her husband and son seemed deaf to her histrionics. In this calm, businesslike atmosphere, such emotion seemed completely out of place.

"Oh, Ted! Ted! Te-ed!" she lamented, as though the boy was about to face a firing squad rather than a journey to Bangkok. "Oh, Ted!"

Other travellers walked briskly by, not even pausing to see what the matter was.

Valerie was as churned up as Ed's mother but she was determined to conceal it, at least until her son was out of sight.

The moment came suddenly.

They handed in their rucksacks. There were no queues. The place was virtually deserted, eerie.

After almost fleeting embraces, they were gone. To travel round the world.

"Bye Mum," said James, over his shoulder. "I'll email."

There was a brief wave before passport control, but no last glance over their shoulders. The boys were looking forward, not back.

Valerie noticed that Ed's father did not put a comforting arm around his wife.

"It's so far," she whimpered, almost accusingly to Valerie, as if she was responsible for the departure of her son and had picked the destination.

"Frances," said David Hardingly, crisply. "I think it's time to go now."

She took off towards the Ladies, leaving the pair of them standing awkwardly.

"Your wife is taking it very hard," commented Valerie. "But I am sure time will fly."

"It already has flown," he said. "That's part of the problem …"

"Yes … it doesn't seem a moment since they started at the Grammar school does it?"

There were a few moments of silence.

"Well, if you hear from Ed, will you let me know? I have a feeling James won't be that good at keeping in touch and it will be lovely to know how they are getting on."

"Of course, and vice versa. If you hear from James," said David. "Here, have my card. It has my email."

Valerie took the card and tucked it into her pocket.

She scribbled her own email address on the back of a scrap of paper and handed it to him.

Frances Hardingly had meanwhile reappeared, her eyes marginally less swollen and her lipstick freshly applied.

"I'm going back to the office," she said to her husband, ignoring Valerie.

She turned her back on them both and marched briskly towards the exit and a sign saying "TAXIS".

"Can I offer you a lift somewhere?" offered David Hardingly.

"You're very kind. But I've got a ticket for the Heathrow Express," she said.

"Well, let's keep in touch," he replied eagerly. "And see if we can keep track of the boys!"

They shook hands and walked away in opposite directions.

A few weeks went by and the boys had not been in touch.

Just as she had dreaded, Valerie's house became a series of unused rooms rather than a home. She tried to avoid going into James's bedroom. His books, computer and speakers sat waiting for his return but other objects were stronger reminders that her son had grown up and moved on: a train set still laid out on the floor but not played with for half a decade and a huge fluffy dinosaur stuffed under the bed. These were the things of childhood that sooner or later would have to be given away.

In cheap clip-frames there were montages of images with class-mates as well as dozens of shots from holidays taken with his cousins in Cornwall. Sitting on his desk in a tarnished silver frame was a photograph of his father, whom he admitted he no longer remembered. Next to that was something that hugely touched her: a picture of herself with James. He had been age 14 at that time, the moment when he had overtaken his mother in height.

On a cork board behind his bed, James had put up a map of the world. Five bright red pins marked the countries he had been to, which included England. "I want it covered," he said "As though it's come out in a rash!" he said. She often felt guilty that she hadn't been able to afford to take them on foreign holidays, but she hoped that James could make up for that now.

In the first week after James's departure, she got rid of an old clock because the sound of its ticking in the void almost deafened her. In the second week she volunteered to do overtime in her job as manager of the doctor's surgery. There was really nothing to go home for except to feed the cat, and herself of course, but cooking for one was a dispiriting exercise. She would always have described herself as "very slim" but now, when she looked in the mirror, she saw someone bordering on "skinny".

Every day she looked out for an email from James, and for three weeks felt a daily sting of disappointment. One day, though, her spirits brightened. There was an email headed: "*The boys*". It was from David Hardingly.

"Just wondering whether you had heard anything yet?" he began chattily. "I haven't."

The use of the first person immediately intrigued her. She replied straightaway.

"No news so far, but I saw one of their mates from school and he had seen on Facebook that they were in Ko Samu. So that's good."

"Nice of them to let us know," came back the immediate reply. "By the way it's Koh Samui."

"Thanks for the spelling correction. I don't know any of these places."

"Well let me know if you hear any more of them – even if it's indirectly."

Valerie carried on with her day, a little more at ease now. Even if James was bad at keeping in touch, at least she had someone to share the anxiety with.

For the next few weeks, they emailed. From time to time, one or other of them had had a text or a brief email sent from an internet cafe somewhere in Asia, just letting the parents know that they were alive and well and having the time of their lives. In a month or so they aimed to be in Australia. Whenever one of these messages came, Valerie and David forwarded them to each other straightaway.

One day, David surprised her.

"I'm at a loose end next week," his message read. "Shall we meet?"

Valerie could not think of a reason why not. It was easy to forward emails, but perhaps he had received a postcard and wanted to share it with her.

They met at a very traditional trattoria in Wimbledon, not far from where Valerie lived, and their conversation focused on the boys.

"Has Ed's mother got used to him being away?" Valerie asked, feeling it would be impolite not to refer to the woman's grief. "She was very upset. I thought afterwards that she must have thought I was rather callous."

For a moment David put his fork down. Until then he had been using it to wind spaghetti carbonara in a way that had struck her as being rather expert.

"I have absolutely no idea," he answered. "We've hardly spoken since he left."

"Oh," said Valerie, trying to conceal her surprise.

"As soon as Ed had gone," he continued. "I think we both realised that he had held our marriage together. Without him around, there was very little left."

"That's so sad," said Valerie, consolingly.

"To be honest, it's not such a tragedy. I don't even think Ed will be surprised."

"But it's a big deal," said Valerie. "Even if he's not surprised, he'll be a bit upset, won't he?"

"I think he's beyond that now," replied David. "She did more or less abandon us both for fifteen years."

"How do you mean?"

"Her work. She never put us first. Neither me nor Ed. Not for a minute. In the end I gave up my job so that I could look after him and the house. That was fine. I did it willingly. But she never came back from the office before midnight. And she left again by six thirty."

"What does she do?"

"Lawyer," he answered.

"And she never took holidays, so we used to go off to things together, just me and Ed."

"So … why was she so upset to see him go off on his travels, then?"

"Remorse. That's what I think it was. Just remorse mixed in with a huge helping of regret."

Valerie sat looking at her food. Thinking of all those years with James, struggling to bring him up alone and yet never once wishing to escape from the task. She understood exactly why Ed's mother had been overwhelmed by emotion, watching her son walk away, and knowing that it was now simply too late to have that time again. Valerie understood perfectly why she had behaved like a woman in mourning.

"Poor woman," she said, thinking aloud.

"Poor woman?"

"I'm just thinking of what she missed out on," said Valerie, feeling she needed to justify her reaction.

"You're right. Those years of bringing Ed up, I wouldn't have traded them in for all the millions my wife was earning. But she could never see it."

They both continued to eat.

"I did suggest that she should pull back a bit on a couple of occasions, but she wouldn't hear of it," said David. "And there was never any question of having another child. It was as though she resented even having had one."

"That's a great pity," reflected Valerie aloud, "For both of you."

"It's just the way it was," he said. "A way of life."

It was clear from his tone of voice that there was no bitterness, just resignation.

David deftly turned his fork into another section of pasta.

"She's moved out of the house now and is in the process of buying another one," he added.

"Just like that?" queried Valerie. "You make it sound so easy."

"When you work at that pace, at least you don't do it for nothing," he said, reflectively. "You're well 'compensated'."

"Money can solve problems as well as create them, can't it …?" said Valerie.

"Absolutely," said David, looking down at his plate and continuing to eat.

It seemed a natural moment for her to share her own situation. Perhaps it was a feminine trait, but she felt that one confidence demanded another in exchange.

"I've been on my own for a long time," she said.

Although they had never spoken before their first meeting at Terminal 5, Valerie knew that David might have seen her alone at school concerts and speech days.

"How long?" he asked.

"Nearly two decades," she replied. "My husband died when James was a baby. It was very tough at the beginning, but I got used to it, eventually. I had plenty to occupy me."

David nodded with concern and understanding, his eyes more than adequately conveying his reaction.

He insisted on settling the bill that evening.

"But only if you'll let me pay another time," said Valerie.

Within a few days, they were sharing further emails sent by their sons.

"Shall we meet for dinner next week?" David asked.

Valerie did not hesitate.

"It makes me feel more in touch with the boys," said Valerie, as they sat down in a corner table of a tapas bar in Islington.

"Same for me," agreed David.

It was during this second meeting that David realised that Valerie had hardly travelled.

"Somehow the opportunity never arose," she murmured, blushing slightly. "Nor the money really."

She felt embarrassed to admit that the only foreign country she had ever seen was France, but David understood without her needing to explain that it had not been by choice. He was aware, because Ed had been on them too, that James had always been given the chance to go on school trips to explore Ancient Greece, Egypt, Jordan and even on a rugby tour of South Africa, and realised now that this had been at a great cost to his mother.

For subsequent dinners, Valerie always allowed David to suggest where they should meet. She had about as much knowledge of restaurants in London as she did of bistros in Paris. Eating out had been something saved for birthdays or celebration of exam results. David, by contrast, was a walking directory of restaurants and picked a different one each time. After a peripatetic childhood with parents in the diplomatic service, he had developed a passion for foreign food.

He took her on a journey of culinary exploration and she went very willingly. They began with French, Spanish, Portuguese, Greek and even Belgian. Then they moved further afield, starting with Indian, Sri Lankan and afterwards Thai, Vietnamese, Cantonese and Malaysian. Once they had finished with the spicy flavours of Asia they moved to South American and David introduced her to Argentinian, Bolivian, Chilean and even Peruvian cuisine, though he admitted that the latter, with the waiters in fancy dress, was probably more of a gimmick than a truly authentic establishment.

Valerie enjoyed them all, except perhaps the Malaysian, which she admitted to finding rather too spicy.

The months passed and they ate their way round the world several times. Conversation always flowed but focused on what they were eating or what news they had received from the boys. These subjects were their common link.

Just over five months after their departure, James and Ed emailed to say that they would be back in five days.

"Let's meet at the Champagne Bar," suggested David in an email. "They serve wonderful Norwegian smoked salmon there."

For the second time in her life, Valerie arrived at Terminal 5. As she perched on her stool, glancing from time to time at the clock, she found herself doing a countdown. This time, the passing minutes led her closer to a moment she wished for.

"Thanks, David." she said. "Time passed much faster than I thought it would. And I think all our meals together helped."

"I'm sure they did," said David quietly. "Look, I wondered …"

Valerie glanced up. Flight BK 469 from Lima had landed and the bags were already in the hall. David allowed Valerie to pay the bill for the first time in six months.

"Let's go," she said, slipping off her stool.

Minutes later James and Ed came through immigration and towards the barrier. On their faces was a mixture of economy class exhaustion and pleasure at seeing their parents again. Smiles beamed from faces that were darkened by sunshine and dirt.

It was hard to embrace someone with a backpack attached to them, but James folded his mother in a crushing embrace.

"Hello Mum," he said.

Both boys were eager to get home and the farewells between them all were perfunctory.

It was only on the train that James looked at his mother properly for the first time.

"So, Mum," he said. "What did you get up to?"

She smiled.

"You know," she said. "Work. The garden. Usual things."

"Well, you look great."

And she did. In the months during which he had been away she had put on weight and no longer had the gaunt look that had characterised her features for so many years.

It was a great novelty having James home again. She enjoyed the pre-term preparations, the shopping for brightly coloured bedding, mugs and stationery, and for a new suit for formal dinners in college. She passed many evenings looking at photographs and listening to her son's anecdotes and descriptions of the people he had met and the things he had seen, all of them the highest, longest or widest in the world. More of the red pins were added to the world map.

The weeks passed quickly and by October they were saying goodbye again. This time he would be a mere few hundred miles away, rather than thousands, but once again a blanket of loneliness descended over her.

A week or so later, she noticed an email from David. She felt a shockwave of excitement.

In the subject box was not:

"*The boys*"

as in the past, but:

"*Valerie Smith*"

"Now the boys have started term, I wondered if you might like to meet for a meal."

She would never have had the courage to propose it, having assumed that their meals together ended with the boys' travels, but, without hesitation, she replied:

"I would love to. Where do you suggest?"

"I was thinking of a Greek taverna?"

"That would be very nice. I am free all next week. Let me know where to meet."

She found herself checking her inbox at least four times before a reply eventually came. For a full five minutes she stared at it, not really believing her eyes.

"Terminal 5," came the reply.

She stared at the message for a full five minutes. There were no Greek restaurants at Heathrow.

She took time off work to queue in person for a passport (her first in fifteen years) and the following week found herself at Departures, once again with a rapidly beating heart. Across the empty space, she soon spotted the distinctive figure of David. He was so familiar but still so unknown.

"Hello Valerie," he said, taking her hand. "It's your turn to see more of the world."

"Yes," she replied, smiling. "I'm ready now."

VICTORIA HISLOP'S FIRST NOVEL, *THE ISLAND*, SOLD 2 MILLION COPIES WORLDWIDE. HER SUBSEQUENT NOVELS, *THE THREAD* AND *THE RETURN*, HAVE BEEN TRANSLATED INTO THIRTY LANGUAGES. SHE IS MARRIED WITH TWO CHILDREN AND LIVES IN LONDON, KENT AND CRETE.

CITY OF GHOSTS

John Gray

It must have been around ten years ago that I saw what seemed like an apparition from the past. Travelling to the airport from a seminar in Brussels, my taxi was stuck in traffic. I had left plenty of time for the journey and was flicking through the pages of a newspaper when I noticed a strange figure. Dressed in what looked like rags, a man of indeterminate age and nationality was threading his way slowly between the cars. He gave no sign of selling anything, or trying to gain the attention of the travellers with an eye to begging. It was as if he had wandered into the street from the stage set of an historical drama.

One feature of the figure added to the unreality of the situation. The man was a hunchback. Of course the term is antiquated and it should not be forgotten that the medical condition from which he was suffering can afflict people in the most modern societies. But there was something archaic in the man's halting gait and it was hard to avoid the impression that this was a phantom from earlier times. The apparition was visible for less than a minute. It was some time after it had vanished from view that it occurred to me that it might actually be a spectre from Europe's future – a future of unravelling and disorder quite different from the vision of increasing cooperation prevalent at the time.

The exact provenance of the meeting I had been attending has slipped from memory. What I recall is how remote from reality the discussions seemed to me to be. The permanence of the European Union was assumed without question, and nearly everyone present was sublimely confident that the new single currency (which was coming into circulation around that time) would eventually embrace every EU member with the possible exception of Britain. The EU was continuing to expand, bringing in countries with very different histories and circumstances, and even then, when I was less of a Eurosceptic than I am now, I found this certainty slightly eerie.

One of the few conversations I recall with any clarity had to do with Turkey becoming an EU member, and I was struck by the unshakable belief of the bureaucrats and officials who make up the European elite that nothing could stop this happening. No one asked what would be done if one or more countries held referenda in which full Turkish membership was rejected. The assumption appeared to be that no such decision could be accepted as final. The elite would press on with the accession process, and any popular opposition that existed would be overridden. Yet while everyone took it for granted that Turkey's accession was inevitable, no one seemed to have given any thought to the problems that accession might bring. When I ventured to ask whether the extension of the EU to the borders of Iraq might pose some dangers there was an awkward silence and the discussion moved on quickly to other issues. It was striking that the inclusion of a region straddling so many geopolitical fault-lines – the oil deposits of northern Iraq and the Kurdish separatist movements that are active in the region, for example – should be seen as unproblematic. Rolling inexorably onwards into a future that was pre-ordained, the EU juggernaut would flatten any obstacles before it. Or so it seemed in Brussels at the time.

Looking back, it is clear that the Euro-capital was possessed by a vision of the future that already belonged in the past. For much of the late twentieth century a powerful body of enlightened opinion held that nationalism and the nation-state were withering away. Institutions like the United Nations – established, like the European Union, in the wake of the Second World War – seemed to show that the world was evolving towards some form of world government. The terrible slaughter of the first half of the twentieth century had shown where narrow and exclusive political loyalties led. Over time, many people believed, an unstoppable process of modernisation would render the national states that had been inherited from the past obsolete.

In securing peace in Europe after the Second World War the European Economic Community – since 1993, the European Union – achieved a necessary and noble goal. Europe had plunged itself and the world into war twice during the first half of the twentieth century. By linking the economic fortunes of the core nations of the European continent inseparably together, similar disasters could be avoided in future. But some visionaries always wanted more than this. In the 1950s, French statesman and diplomat Claude Monnet, one of the fathers of the EU, founded a Committee for a United States of Europe. Europe's nations, he and his followers believed, must be merged together in an American-style federal state. Monnet and others were not simply reacting against the catastrophic effects of Europe's two civil wars. They were acting out a vision of what it means to be modern in which nation-states play an ever-diminishing role.

Unfortunately the highly educated men and women who were gripped by this vision failed to notice that nationalism was still the most powerful force shaping the global scene. The anti-colonial movements that gained power in Asia, Africa and the Middle East after the Second World War did so by overthrowing European power. But their goal was to create their own versions of the European nation-state. Even the communist parties that seized control in China and Vietnam – though dedicated in theory to a creating a world without nations – derived much of their popular support from anti-European nationalism. The United Nations may have been seen by some as a step towards world government, but in fact it proved to be a forum for dozens of new nation-states.

Coming closer to the present, the collapse of communism also demonstrated the enduring power of national loyalties. Many factors contributed to the weakness of the Soviet Union – not least military defeat in Afghanistan. But the USSR began to unravel when it could no longer control events in Poland, where a powerful sense of nationhood animated the Catholic Church and Solidarity, the militant workers organisation.

When the break-up of the Soviet Union was followed by the disintegration of Yugoslavia in the early 1990s, nationalism was again the most powerful force shaping events in Europe. Ethnic cleansing in the Balkans towards the end of the last century had clear precedents in the violent nation-building that occurred in Europe between the two world wars. Many of the European nation-states that achieved self-government after the fall of the Soviet Union were created in the aftermath of the collapse of the Habsburg empire in 1919. The state of Yugoslavia was first created in 1918 as a monarchical regime that included Serbs, Croats and Slovenes. But the state failed to become a nation, and Yugoslav resistance against Nazism during the Second World War was marked by intense conflict between different sections of the partisan forces.

Despite these signs of the persistent force of nationalism, the wars that accompanied the collapse of transnational Yugoslavia took Europe by surprise. Ethnic conflict and mass murder were not supposed to happen in late twentieth-century Europe. In the event, it was not Europe but the US that imposed a kind of peace in the Balkans. Lacking either the will or the logistical capability, the EU was forced to rely on American airpower to end the Yugoslav wars.

The fact that Europe had to turn to the US to settle intra-European conflict is not without significance. For many of its supporters, the European Union is an American-style federal state in the making. The former head of the European Central

Bank, Jean-Claude Trichet, has on several occasions compared the eurozone with the United States. Defending the euro, he has asked rhetorically how the US would work if each of its states had a separate currency. Is not the US like the eurozone in having an economy with widely varying levels of productivity and prosperity? And does not the American federal government act to smooth out these disparities by making transfers between America's states?

Trichet's questions show how far removed the European elites are from historical realities. America achieved independence towards the end of the eighteenth century after a revolutionary war against the British and other European powers, but it only became a modern state after a savage civil war (1861–65) during which the Confederate states attempted to secede from the Union. It was during this period that the dollar became America's national currency. Without these two wars there would be nothing resembling the American state that existed when the US first created a central bank – the American Federal Reserve – in 1913. In turn, the highly cohesive American nation-state that exists today came into being only after the Great Depression and the Second World War had further tilted the balance of power towards the federal government. The American state that Trichet cited as a model for Europe is the product of over two centuries of nation-building.

In contrast, there is no European nation and no sign that any will ever come into being. The eurozone remains what Europe has always been in modern times, a continent of contentious nation-states. The region is now also burdened by a currency that prevents economic disparities between the component economies being resolved by shifts in exchange rates. The result is a rigid structure that exacerbates tensions and has no realistic prospect of long-term survival in its present form.

Having been created in order to become an American-style federal state, the EU is reversing America's course of development. Where the US created a national currency on the back of a pre-existing nation-state, the euro has been created out of nothing by a fractious coalition of national governments. There is no mechanism through which different levels of development can be evened out without agonising austerity in the less developed countries. The current crisis is a consequence of these facts. Economists argue that the eurozone can be stabilised by moving towards a fiscal union in which the spending and debt of all the component states are controlled at a European level. But since the lack of a fiscal union reflects the inverted development of the eurozone itself, there is no possibility of the crisis being settled in this way.

The federal institutions that exist in the US came into being over hundreds of years of sometimes violent conflict. There is not the remotest likelihood that similar institutions can be created in Europe in the near future. On the contrary, there is a realistic prospect that some states will make a disorderly and chaotic exit from the eurozone over the coming years. Though there is no prospect of war, the pressure for deeper integration is working to promote secession and break up the European structures that currently exist.

At the same time, the position of EU countries outside the eurozone is also likely to become untenable. The position of Britain is likely to become increasingly anomalous. If the crisis worsens and the eurozone disintegrates, the impact on Britain's economy and banking system will be large and destabilising. But if something like a federal state develops in the eurozone Britain's situation will be even more untenable, since there is no prospect of the country's inclusion in a European super-state being ratified by a referendum. In the medium to longer-term, the upshot of the eurozone crisis can only be a looser relationship between Britain and Europe – and, quite conceivably, Britain's exit from the EU. In the meantime, the rickety European structures totter from crisis to crisis.

The crisis that has paralysed Europe was not entirely unexpected. Some supporters of the euro have long argued that Europe would become a state only after a succession of crises. The Green leader Joshka Fischer, later German Foreign Minister and Vice-Chancellor and an influential member of the Euro-elite, has been arguing this since the late 1990s. It seems never to have occurred to Fischer, or others who think like him, that such crises might have the opposite effect of fuelling nationalism.

Ironically, the world today has many resemblances to that of the late nineteenth century. The United States is itself a model nineteenth-century state, unwilling to compromise its national sovereignty by signing up to transnational institutions such as the International Criminal Court. China – though still having some resemblances to the Chinese empires of former times – has turned itself into a replica of the culturally cohesive nation-states that developed in nineteenth-century and early twentieth-century Europe. As in the late nineteenth century, there is no super-power that is stronger than all the rest. The US still has military and naval superiority, but since the financial crisis it can no longer afford to intervene wherever it judges its interests to be threatened. America does not rule the world, and neither do any of the other great powers that have emerged. With new players such as China and India, Brazil and Africa, which a century ago were colonially subjugated, the international scene has returned to the way it was before the First World War – a shifting concert of great powers, none of them capable of dominating or controlling the others.

There are those who fear a re-run of the 1930s, and the toxic politics of nationalism that is re-emerging in countries such as Hungary, which though outside the eurozone suffers from many of its economic problems, does have some similarities with that of the 1930s – including a virulent anti-Semitism. There is a real risk that the old poisons of xenophobia will re-enter the political mainstream in other European countries. But the Europe-wide mass movements of the 1930s – communist and fascist – no longer exist, and there is little danger of them returning. The past that is looming into view is an older one, and in a further irony it is European federalists that are speeding the process.

Supposed to seal the fate of European nation-states, the euro has revitalised them. There can be no doubt that commitment to the euro-project remains strong, not least in Germany. Yet Angela Merkel may well prove to be the unwitting historic instrument whereby Germany reverts to something like the position it occupied a century ago, as Europe's most advanced economy, with interests extending far beyond the continent. It is hard to resist the thought that, a decade or so from now, Germany will be what it was at the time of Bismarck, the continent's dominant power, looking out to Russia and Asia for markets and influence.

Whether the euro will collapse in the near future, or limp along for years from one crisis to another, cannot be known. It is possible that electronic money-printing by the European Central Bank will give a devalued version of the currency a new lease of life. Or else the currency will fragment, with a smaller, German-oriented version emerging that is stronger than the one that exists today. What is clear is that the decline of the European project is terminal. Far from being the embodiment of an inexorable process of modernisation, the euro is – like communism – a phantasm projected by nineteenth-century utopian thinking, a dream that imagines the persistent conflicts of history will somehow fade and vanish when in reality they are simply mutating into different forms.

Like that earlier utopia, the euro is bringing to parts of Europe a regime of austerity and poverty of a kind not seen there for generations. In Greece it is producing a reverse form of economic development, in which city-dwellers return to the countryside where they can grow their own food. In Ireland, Spain and Portugal, the result is swelling emigration, as young people leave for countries such as Brazil, Bulgaria and Albania in search of jobs. In Italy, and despite the promises of President Hollande also in France, the security ensured by the welfare state can no longer be counted on. Throughout Europe, prospects that seemed solid and substantial are proving to be chimerical. Instead of being a continent-wide social democracy – Germany or Sweden re-invented on an enormous scale – the Europe that is looming into sight is a continent of fractious nation-states, some of them mired in stagnation, with repeated bouts of austerity triggering social unrest and extremist politics.

I sometimes wonder what became of the man who appeared to me a decade ago as a fleeting apparition. Probably a migrant from the poorer margins of the continent, he was wandering through Europe's capital in what may have been a vain search of a better life. Whatever his fate, he was at home for a time in Brussels, where Europe's elites live surrounded by phantoms of what once seemed to be the future.

JOHN GRAY IS THE AUTHOR OF *STRAW DOGS: THOUGHTS ON HUMANS AND OTHER ANIMALS* AND *THE IMMORTALIZATION COMMISSION: THE STRANGE QUEST TO CHEAT DEATH*. FORMERLY PROFESSOR OF EUROPEAN THOUGHT AT THE LONDON SCHOOL OF ECONOMICS, HE NOW WRITES FULL-TIME.

THE EMPTY CHAIR

Jackie Kay

Robert Anderson wiped the snow from the windscreen of his car. He pulled the newspaper off, good old trick that, and walked carefully round the sides, brushing the snow from the other windows, careful not to slip. He wasn't sure he needed to go out, and it was a palaver with this heavy snow, but he couldn't settle inside either. This winter was the first winter that Bobby had lived through without his wife: the first winter when he didn't find himself saying, "Watch yourself there on the path, dear," or "Do you fancy a bowl of soup?" – when he didn't find himself saying, "You want a read at G2?" "Need anything at the shops?" "Remembered your pills?" "Packed your hearing aid?" "Got your stick?" Had anybody asked him, do you realise that you will miss being able to ask the simplest of questions, he might have grasped their point, but would he have truly understood it? Despite all the friends he'd outlived, he didn't have a clue. He had never allowed himself to dwell on death, too busy enjoying life, so much so that when it came to it, there were questions he couldn't answer about his wife Ailsa after sixty years of marriage.

They had never got round to finding out from each other if they'd prefer a burial or a cremation. (He assumed at first cremation, but he knew she'd always found the final curtain brutal; but then again, at rainy gravesides over the years, she'd often used the word *ghastly*.) But their preference – that was a question that had not come up in conversation, or at least, if it had, it had never reached a conclusion. In the end he opted for burial because she'd always loved reading headstones, walking round graves, even, apparently, when she was a wee girl, trying to imagine people's lives. The graveyard guy had hinted darkly that when his time came, there'd be room enough for two, so that was the clincher. Perhaps, some small part of them was a little superstitious; they believed that if they didn't talk about death in detail, they'd be allowed a few extra years. Those glorious extra retired years would get snuck in, under the radar, as it were and nobody would notice, providing the opportunity to go to South Uist, say, a place he'd always wanted to visit, and see a white goat standing by an old croft; or see *Death of a Salesman* again; or through to Edinburgh for some shows at the fringe. If they just kept their heads down and didn't ask too many questions about coffin choices, cremation versus burial, wreaths or charity donations, Jesus, then those particular cultured atheists would be allowed extra time, maybe they had reckoned. And extra time, like in a football match, was absolutely crucial. It could change things: extra time.

Robert and Ailsa didn't believe in God, and yet somehow they liked the idea of fate, not in a heavy way, more that they leaned towards the spirit of chance, coincidence, and enjoyed the ways human beings randomly connected. For instance, they believed they were fated to have met when they did, all the way on the other side of the world. And when they couldn't have children, they believed they were meant to adopt. And when none of their children got married, they didn't mind. Ailsa said to Bobby not that long ago, "Thank god I never had to decide what to wear for my daughter's or my son's wedding. No silly hat!" He might have liked to walk his only daughter down the aisle, and now that gay weddings were about to become legal that still might be possible. Now that eighty was well behind him, seemed positively young, and sixty like bloody teenage years; now that he was the ripe age of eighty-eight, and the body was starting to actually suffer the effects of what he could only describe as old age, he was taken aback at his sentimentality.

What surprised him most was how important his family was to him now in his old age. He didn't regret any of the factory-gate speeches he'd made, the demonstrations he'd been on, the comrades he'd signed up, the strikes he'd encouraged. What he deeply regretted was once shouting at his five-year-old son when he got his fishing line all tangled up. He regretted that. He wished, looking back, that he'd had more patience as a father, that he'd put in more time. But this was the first winter that he'd lived without Ailsa, sitting beside him in the passenger's side, pushing her hand against the dashboard if she felt he was going too fast. He could see her quite clearly, how she had looked when they first met.

She was a good-looking woman, no doubt about it. A thick head of brown curly hair, right down her back. Sometimes, he'd find himself falling behind her, just to watch her walk. She had, what was the word he was searching for – grace. She had grace. Your mother was a good-looking woman, he'd say to his daughter.

They lived in a street where, one by one, their friends were picked out, it seemed, as if somebody had whispered "*your turn*". Robert knew that to be nonsense, but still when it came to be his wife, Ailsa, dying, he couldn't quite shake this notion. He'd been the man who had crossed the road to take the new widow or widower a pot of soup, a wee half. He was the man who would come back and tell Ailsa that Isabel, Irene, Jeanette, May or Alec was in better or worse shape than they'd imagined. "What more can you do but try and cope? Put the face on, eh?" he'd say and Ailsa would nod, irritably wanting him to stop blocking her view of *Midsomer Murders.*

It'd been Ailsa's turn, he thought, driving his car and wiping the windscreen at the same time. The visibility was poor. He should have stayed at home. He was always planning on giving up driving, like somebody who planned to give up the pipe – too many cars on the road, filthy fumes. He parked up, got his canvas bags out of the boot, a red one and a green one. He hated it if he forgot these bags and would carry things back loose in his arms rather than resort to plastic; Christ the whole planet was suffocating under plastic. Imagine the planet as a person with a plastic bag over their head, by Christ, panicking and puffing for air. That's what she was like in the end, Ailsa, struggling for air. She said it was like drowning.

How anyone can deny the effect of global warming is beyond me, he thought to himself, walking down Great Western Road. Funny, the snow hadn't settled in the town at all. It was just a bit of mush, and sludge. First, the fish shop. He bought a small piece of hake. Soon, he thought, he'd need to give up fish because it was a disgrace, the over-farming of the sea. Maybe he should give it up now? Ditto the car? He walked to Grassroots and bought a sweet and sour loaf. He went into Mellis' and bought two small pieces of cheese his daughter would enjoy if she came to visit before they had a chance to go off. There was a comfort to be found in smelly cheeses. He'd no idea what their names were. If he liked the look of them, he simply pointed and said, a bit of that please. He found himself saying almost out loud, "Anything else we need?" The woman was saying something to him. "Pardon, dear?" he said. "Do you want anything else?" she said. He said, "No thank you, dear, that will be all." He passed first one bank and then another with those holes in the wall that he'd never mastered, though Ailsa had expressed a desire to try one a wee while ago. And he'd sung to her half-jokingly, *but the banks are made of marble/with a guard at every door/And the vaults are stuffed with silver/that the farmer sweated for.*

And he got back into his car, after carefully placing his messages in the boot, and put it into first gear and took off. He didn't have, had never had, power steering and turning the corners gave his arms exercise. Ailsa had always wanted a four-door car. Was that a regret now, that he'd never got her one? In the name of Christ, if you could only regret material things, you were in danger. If you, an old socialist, should now at the age of eighty-eight, for goodness sake, be regretting a commodity you didn't buy your wife? The market forces ruled the heads of socialists even, and it wasn't any more about need; it was all about want. What was it that Willy Loman says again? What was that line of his that was so touching? *You end up worth more dead than alive*, Christ that was it.

Since his wife died, it seemed the only thing that partly settled his stomach was to remember stories, his own or ones he'd read or seen. On the phone the other night, he'd said to his daughter, "that guy Don Draper, is he for real? Was the guy deluded? *Was he aff his heid?*" Or he'd find himself saying to his daughter, out of the blue, "There was the time when your mother was rightly angry with me for forgetting our wedding anniversary. I'd had a meeting with the ship builders and it ran late and when I came in she was all dolled up sat in the chair and she'd been crying and you came hurling down the stairs, at eleven at night, and gave me an earful? Remember?" He'd find himself going down one lane and then the next and he wasn't quite sure what it was he was looking for. It wasn't as if he was trying to get to what actually happened and who was right and who was wrong; no, it was as if the intimacy in the memory, whatever it was, confirmed him, that he had been loved. Maybe that was the word he was distractedly looking for. In the distance, he could see the snow lying thick on the Campsies. Beautiful. The words *I love you*, were they for English men, or middle-class men or young men? Not men like himself who found they sat awkward in his mouth. He doubted he'd ever managed to write the words in any of the cards he'd written Ailsa over the years, still less say them out loud, though he'd always found a way to come up with a merry quip. These days, young men probably tweeted their love. But she knew anyway, Ailsa, she knew.

He suddenly remembered he'd forgotten to get a copy of the *Financial Times*. He'd told himself he'd treat himself this Saturday. Was it worth turning around? Was it worth turning the car around? He pulled into a petrol station and set back off into town. He felt reckless, wild even. It was snowing again, and the flakes swirled in front of him. What a turn he'd given himself, suddenly heading back into town when he'd only just left. But there was no one waiting for him and nobody to notice how late he was.

He walked down Byres Road towards the newsagents and wondered if he should stop in a cafe. They always stopped when they were out shopping for either a cup of coffee or a bowl of soup, but mainly to let Ailsa rest her legs, because she was shaky on her pins. Now that there was no Ailsa to rest her legs, and no Ailsa to have a conversation with over coffee, did he actually need to stop? This was what he was finding and it was a strange thing. He was now having to think odd things like "Am I the kind of man that likes to stop when out shopping for a cup of coffee?" And the answer was *No*. He found his needs had actually shrunk and the daily jobs had dwindled too. He had no Ailsa to pick up from the hairdressers, no pills from the doctors, no hospital appointments. It was a strange emptiness but it was less noticeable when he was out in the street than it was back in the house, with the armchair opposite him empty. At least he thought it was, but when, on the odd occasion, he did sit down in a café for a bite to eat, he'd find that emptiness even more remarkable, even if he made a point of going to a place that he'd never been to with Ailsa. There was the empty chair. It seemed he could carry it with him. It seemed if he just picked one at random and lifted it with him wherever he went, not a whole armchair, he wouldn't manage that, didn't have the strength, but maybe just a simple wooden-back chair, then he would be happy.

It didn't seem right; his friends found it awkward even mentioning her name. Of course he knew that they were trying their best. But wiping Ailsa out, pretending that she'd never existed, shifting uncomfortably when he got out old photos of Ailsa, Ailsa on the ferry to Harris, Ailsa in their back garden ... He found himself putting them up around the house, tucking them into existing frames with paintings in them, so that she appeared in the corner of things, and when Frank, or Alec, or Morris came round he would point out one or the other to them, and they would shift, and say, ill at ease, aye, that's a good likeness.

So why not stage his own last protest, he thought. He was the man who only five years ago had joined the Green Party, who only twenty or so years before that had joined the Democratic Left, who as a young man had been imprisoned for protesting about Polaris, who had been on many anti-apartheid demos, CND marches, Upper Clyde Shipbuilders rallies, who had gone to see Madame Allende in George Square, who had listened to Paul Robeson sing in Carnegie Hall.

That Saturday, the snow was still lying thick in his street when he got home, and still falling, and it was a struggle carting the wooden chair across the road to Isabel's house, Isabel who had invited him in for his dinner. But he managed it. He carried it carefully and placed it outside her front porch. Then he made his way back across the road to fetch the bottle of red wine. It would have been impossible for him to carry both at the same time. He stood outside her door and rang the bell. He handed her the wine. She said, "Bobby, you needn't have bothered bringing wine. Come in. Come in."

He struggled with the chair, through the door and put it down by the table that Isabel had already set. Isabel said nothing about his empty chair; but that wasn't quite what he wanted. What did he want? Did he want her to pretend it was Ailsa? Christ, no. But he didn't want folk to just say nothing about it. He wanted them to say something. Even if it was, "What do you think you're playing at you daft bugger?" Something. He found himself searching his store of anecdotes. "Did I tell you of the time when Ailsa," he said to Isabel and she looked wary as if she didn't want to hear the same story again. "Try me," she said. And he found himself suddenly weeping with laughter. "It was funny, Christ, what a laugh ..." Isabel nodded like she understood this need to tell stories. She had been widowed for years. He'd never realised, all this time when he'd wanted the recently bereaved not to weep, to keep composed, he had never realised what it cost them. Christ, he'd had no idea. He wanted to apologise to all the bereaved over the years, the old comrades and their wives. He just hadn't realised. Grief, Jesus Christ, it was like a bloody nuclear bomb. He felt blasted by it. He managed to shave, to eat, to sleep, but all the time, even, at the age of eighty-eight, he felt frail, not in the way that he had felt frail when Ailsa was alive, with his bony shoulders and skin hanging over his belly, but frail inside his mind, He could still do his crossword puzzle, and read a book, but his mind was dashing hither and thither and it seemed it was always trying to find Ailsa.

He stopped in the middle of his story. He took a large slurp of wine and said to Isabel. "What do you think of my empty chair?" And Isabel, nonplussed at the intimacy of this question, said nothing. There was an awkward pause. "I think your chair's lovely. Simply elegant, beautiful Bobby." "Do you think so?" he said. "Absolutely," she said.

And he took another glug of wine. When he left the house with his empty chair, Isabel said, careful now. He carried it across the road: the snow was thick and quiet, secretive. Strangely, carrying the chair into his house somehow made the empty armchair less stark, and easier too to suddenly hear Ailsa's voice. He heard Ailsa laughing, *Do you wish you'd told me you loved me or do you* not *wish you'd told me you loved me?* The only thought that consoled him was that Ailsa had never had to go through this for him. She'd never had to grieve him. She'd got off really, more or less Scot-free. He wondered where that came from, that expression, Scot-free? He put the empty chair next to the armchair and he opened his blinds and looked out at the numb snow on the quiet street. Then he closed his blinds again and climbed the stairs to bed and got out his book. Both of them had loved Alice Munro stories, and so he started to read one, which he must have read before, and was perhaps attracted again by the title, "Runaway", about a young woman and a goat. He could picture the goat. Do you remember, Ailsa, he thought, that time we went to Arran and attempted Goat Fell? It was steep, steeper than we thought. And it occurred to him that, in a strange way, the conversation could continue.

JACKIE KAY'S MOST RECENT COLLECTION OF SHORT STORIES, *REALITY, REALITY*, WAS PUBLISHED THIS YEAR BY PICADOR. HER MEMOIR *RED DUST ROAD* WON THE SCOTTISH BOOK AWARD AND *FIERE* WAS SHORTLISTED FOR THE COSTA.

MILL LANE

Andrew Motion

Mill Lane which was rose brick rubble and motor cars
squeezed into angry cubes to start with, then ripped up
and replaced by a river of fascinating tar that appeared

wet but only became so at the height of high summer,
then tar covered almost entirely with pale fawn gravel
that poured as evenly as sand from the back of a truck

so it just glittered through here and there like a river,
a black river running beneath everything in the world:
Mill Lane was a serious distraction and sliced through

the houses alongside home where I came to my senses
before continuing to the dozen Nissen huts abandoned
behind tall gates and chicken wire I am coming to next.

*

But first the hedge bounding our side of Mill Lane
which was holly and beech stitched tight together,
the beech leaves nutty to chew, holly always lethal

except for two blackbirds holed up there in secret
they thought, although chicks weeping and weeping
whenever these parents flitted, then the careful lift

of their glittering armour, always would make plain
the nest flowing over with young but not quite over-
flowing, the rubbery beaks revolting or do I mean

beautiful, before I was back on track and within sight
of the stained miserable huts and wire, but instead
turned to the field where two ponies stood waiting.

*

One chestnut pony and the second chestnut a shade
darker or not, maybe some trick of afternoon light,
taking shelter beneath a voluminous hawthorn tree

arching in full flower because it is always Spring
now I think of it, and individual flakes of blossom
are straggling onto their manes, backs and shoulders

without them noticing because they notice nothing,
they exist merely by standing still and side by side
as though one was a reflection of the other and the air

has hardened into a mirror which showed them alone,
and not me looking, or the blossoming hawthorn tree,
or the breeze that blew and knocked the blossom down.

*

In the end however I come to what cannot be avoided,
these padlocked gates in the fence and the huts beyond
we never spoke of at home and therefore never existed

until we left Mill Lane when the news broke that once
prisoners of war lived here – men I then saw strolling
in circles or stretched on the sorry grass to keep watch

on the same cloud for hours, while in the world beyond
I drifted towards them along the river under the gravel
which claimed my whole attention if not the blackbirds

fussing inside their dominion, and the chestnut ponies
that never moved, and the hawthorn blossom still falling,
until I reached the gates and stopped dead in my ignorance.

ANDREW MOTION IS PROFESSOR OF CREATIVE WRITING AT ROYAL HOLLOWAY, UNIVERSITY OF LONDON. HE WAS POET LAUREATE FROM 1999 TO 2009 AND HIS MOST RECENT COLLECTION OF POEMS IS *THE CUSTOMS HOUSE* (FABER & FABER, 2012).

THE MENACE OF MILE END

Simon Van Booy

Mr. Baxter did not like people very much, so when he was woken up one night by someone shouting in the street, it was with more annoyance than concern that he untangled himself from the sheets, felt for his glasses and shuffled quietly to the far window of the flat, which he always kept open.

Mr. Baxter was the only private resident on a London street of men's tailors and barbershops. His small house – once home to the Saint James's Church clergy, was built in 1762 on a narrow hill against the back wall of the church.

Whether by accident or inspired planning, the church sometimes appeared to embrace the little house with two arms conjured from an arrangement of shadow.

After two hundred years, the clergy relocated to the suburbs, and 35A Jermyn Street was sold to an American business tycoon because it was collapsing.

During renovation, an unexploded shell from World War II was found in a sewer. Jermyn Street was evacuated for three hours. The old barbers stood awkwardly in aprons on Piccadilly, remembering the many days of falling bombs, when bodies washed through the underground tunnels like heavy dolls, and people shared bars of chocolate or took turns on a cigarette.

The business tycoon, John Bray, had gifted the house to Mr. Baxter some years before.

Children would consider them both to be old men, but they were at least twenty years apart.

The tycoon seldom left his estate in East Sussex and lived only for his blind granddaughter in New York.

Mr. Baxter had lived on Jermyn Street for seventeen years. He was known to his commercial neighbours only by sight. Passing their windows every day on his way home from St. James's Park, he caught their attention with a falling trouser hem or an umbrella in need of repair.

Despite his age, Mr. Baxter was still heavy and muscular, with enormous hands that he kept awkwardly at his sides, as if they were props of some kind.

His eyes were deep blue and quicker than his body, which made him appear more nervous than he actually was. There were no longer any traces of brown in his hair, and his bones often ached – depending on the weather.

When the rain disrupted his daily walk, Mr. Baxter set a chair beside the window. There were usually people on the pavement below, and the shop windows of Jermyn Street glowed with promise. A street florist called out in Latin as a way to draw people in, and an endless stream of red buses grumbled in the heavy traffic of Piccadilly Circus.

When the shops closed, Mr. Baxter sat in the dark. Small women came and vacuumed with chrome Hoovers. Then they sat in their aprons and unwrapped sandwiches. One of the cleaners was pregnant.

In the morning, after a few hours' sleep on the settee, Mr. Baxter drank his tea standing up. Window cleaners and their sons sloshed along Jermyn Street with buckets and rags. Sometimes they whistled, and the sound fell from their mouths like silver thread.

Men smoked and unloaded vans, while others scavenged through piles of rubbish. Chefs chatted on phones in their kitchen whites, while student waiters chained bicycles with plastic bags tied over the seat.

When it was time for his daily walk in St. James's Park, Mr. Baxter dressed methodically and went out. Once in the park, he liked to find an empty bench that wasn't too damp.

Clouds passed above in lines of white shoulders.

Mr. Baxter wondered where they were going. He stared at them the way an illiterate stares at words in a sentence.

There is a deep lake in the middle of St. James's Park. Long ago, when you could smell London before you saw it and people lived in soggy, straw-roofed houses on London Bridge – it was common to bring your wishes to the lake, and then cast them like nets.

Children still gather at the edge of the water. They often stand quite still, their eyes fixed with more feeling than sight.

Sometimes Mr. Baxter lingered at the lake but, with nothing to wish for, he stared at the swans folding their wings, or at the women in headscarves tossing crumbs from their pockets.

He secured his coat at the waist by knotting a belt. The coat was very old. Sometimes he wore it over his dressing gown to bed. There were stains around the hem, and also at the front where he had missed the toilet. He wore glasses to see. They were square with gold frames and a brown tint to each lens that was once fashionable. Sometimes, a flake of his skin would lodge on the glass.

There was a time when Mr. Baxter was quite fashionable – quite outgoing – quite a known face in London.

But that was long ago, and the man woken by someone screaming in the street – who shuffled across the kitchen from his settee bed to find out what was going on – looked much older than he actually was.

The person below Mr. Baxter's window was shouting in Jamaican patois. He was about sixteen years old and pulled at his short dreadlocks as though he expected them to come off in his hands. Puddles had hardened into ice. Mr. Baxter wondered if he might slip on one.

He listened to the boy and spread both his hands on the kitchen table like a great pianist, trying to understand what he could so clearly hear.

A couple strolling home from Wiltons Restaurant stopped talking for a moment and crossed to the other side of the road.

It would have been much quieter in the small bedroom at the back of Mr. Baxter's house, but for years he had slept every night on the settee. The expensive floral cotton sheets and pillowcases, purchased one summer afternoon at Liberty, lay smooth and undisturbed, like an envelope sealed long ago upon a letter that was never written.

When the young man returned to Jermyn Street two nights later, Mr. Baxter listened from his pillow in a sort of daze. It was bitterly cold. A string of black taxis roared up Jermyn Street, their heavy diesel engines rattling the windows on one side.

'This can't go on,' Mr. Baxter thought. 'I was in the middle of a bloody dream.'

He folded back his sheets and sat on the edge of the settee. 'All I'm asking for is a bit of peace,' he thought, fumbling for his glasses. 'And now I've got some mad bastard out there.'

The pubs were still open. The sound of people walking echoed through his flat like disorderly music. Voices too – animated by wine and the excitement of a fierce cold – filled his head, casting his thoughts back to other versions of himself, when the web of Christmas lights strung across Regent Street illuminated what he had, rather than what he'd lost.

When Mr. Baxter unlatched the window and cautiously peered down at the figure for a third night, he noticed a plastic bag of clothes. The arm of a sweater reached out as if trying to escape. Mr. Baxter shook his head in reproach.

"Some people," he said to himself. "Are a bleedin' nuisance."

Then for a week the man didn't come.

Jermyn Street was a place of general quiet.

It was so cold, that the government told people not to go out. The demand for coal and wood was unprecedented. Elderly people were found dead at home sitting upright in their chairs.

Mr. Baxter spent the week lying awake, wondering where he was. Then he lay awake wondering who he was.

The night he returned, Mr. Baxter pulled on his dressing gown and hurried to the window. It was still cold. The man below wore neither gloves nor hat.

"What an idiot," Mr. Baxter thought. "His own bloody fault if he dies of cold out there."

The few people who were out, hurried home in clouds of their own breath.

Workmen emptied bins or wheeled cages of cheese and artichokes into Fortnum & Mason, then roared off in vans. A few shops away, the sound of laughing. Mr. Baxter leaned out to see. In the distance, a woman and a man struggling to walk in a straight line – then the woman sat down in the middle of the road. The man pulled on her arm, but she lay down and laughed.

When a car entered Jermyn Street going too fast, the young man below Mr. Baxter's window began to shout, "Car, car, car" like some strange bird.

Somehow understanding – the drunks lifted their heads and dragged their bodies from the dazzle of headlamps. They watched the car roar up Jermyn Street for a few moments, as if trying to make sense of it. Then it disappeared, bound for other lives less fortunate.

After the drunks went away, the young man commenced shouting in Jamaican patois again.

Mr. Baxter noticed a fork on the kitchen table. He rested his fingers on it.

Many years ago, Mr. Baxter's father would sometimes wake him up very late at night. He dressed with his eyes half-closed, but fully aware what was going to happen. He was only a child, but understood that it would have been worse not to go.

Under his bed was a box of toy cars, a cricket bat, and a few broken Airfix Spitfire models. There was also a pennant that was frayed but still meant a great deal to him. He'd won it at the seaside.

After going downstairs, Mr. Baxter sat squarely in front of his father at the kitchen table, trying not to blink, and slowly hardening into the statue of a boy – so that when he did blink and the fork came down on the backs of his hands repeatedly, there was only a vague feeling that parts of his body were on fire.

Sometimes his father would laugh, or smash a bottle, or split a cupboard door with his elbow. Sometimes, he would take everything out of the fridge and leave it on the floor.

The next day, the teachers wanted to know why Charlie Baxter couldn't hold his pencil – why the backs of his hands were black and yellow. He was made to stand in a corner until ready to confess. But it was their secret, and, in some beautiful child way, the young Mr. Baxter felt that his father respected him for it.

He went back to bed. It was warm under the blankets, and his feet were hot under the covers. He thought for a minute about what had happened outside with the speeding car. Having no curtains, streetlight washed over his things and pooled against furniture that blocked its way.

Before falling asleep, Mr. Baxter wondered if anger is just another form of crying.

In the morning, he cooked a breakfast that was much larger than usual. He put the remains on a plate in the fridge. Then he washed the frying pan and hung it above the sink. It dripped into a tea towel that was folded on the counter for the sole purpose of catching drops.

On his walk that day, Mr. Baxter noticed more birds than usual. They congregated at one side of the pond where park officials had broken the ice with heavy sticks.

Mr. Baxter stood for some time on the narrow bridge that stretched over the lake. On one side, up past the blowing bare trees and brown frozen water, was Buckingham Palace. On the other side, a slow rise of gray marble into Whitehall: a few towers with peaks; two flags snapping in the breeze like squares of blood.

It was Mr. Baxter's favorite place to stand and think. The view had not changed for centuries, despite love and death, war, hot summers, disappointment, wind, and quiet days of nothing much.

Three nights later, Mr. Baxter stirred a pot of tea and listened at the window. The moon was out and etched the man's outline against the darkness.

Why hadn't someone called the police and reported a lunatic disturbing the peace? It was now so irritating that he wanted to throw his mug of tea at the man's head. Bits of mug on the ground like heavy chalk. He imagined pulling the man's arms off like clay, and then his legs, and then his head; stuffing them into his black bag of clothes, then tossing it into the icy Thames.

For the first time in many years, Mr. Baxter felt violence bubbling to the surface of his life. But while considering an extreme course of action that he would never take, a bottle struck and shattered against the wall of St. James's Church. Mr. Baxter looked out and saw another bottle flash with streetlight then land silently on the bag of clothes. Three figures stormed across the road toward the young man, fists spinning.

Mr. Baxter stood, shaking, his feet half in his slippers.

He looked desperately around his kitchen for something among his cutlery and chipped pans. Then his lips tightened and Mr. Baxter knotted the string on his dressing gown.

By the time he got down to the street, there were clothes everywhere, and the boy was a ball on the ground. When a heavy old man in dressing gown and slippers suddenly appeared, the three men stopped kicking. For a moment, just the sight of Mr. Baxter seemed to deter them. Then one came at him with a broken bottle.

But Mr. Baxter was once quite a dangerous man. He grew up in the East End.

For a few years he was Twiggy's bodyguard, then an American business tycoon's, then private events, then nightclubs.

He had stopped working seventeen years before, after waking up in the Royal Free hospital.

"Who got me?" He said to the nurse. But it was painful even to chuckle.

"No one got you Rambo," she said. "You had a heart attack."

Later, she brought flowers wrapped in newspaper and arranged them herself in the vase.

Some nights she stayed a bit later and read to him. No one had ever read to him. It was like a world within a world, and he felt free of his troubles.

About this time, he also had another visitor. John Bray, the millionaire he once worked for, whose family Mr. Baxter had saved from a violent kidnap attempt. Mr. Baxter didn't know how John found out he was there. They hadn't seen each other for decades.

John brought chocolates and they talked about their lives, about getting older. Then they sat in silence reading different sections of the newspaper. Sometimes the nurse brought cups of tea. Then one afternoon, John asked his old bodyguard if he could tell him about what happened to him during the war.

Mr. Baxter listened carefully.

Before his discharge, some of the staff had a party for Mr. Baxter. He had been there a month. People had grown used to him. They all knew he would never work again, but didn't say it. After the paper plates were cleaned up and people had gone back to the ward, Mr. Bray opened his briefcase and took out some legal papers. He said he needed one last favor, and that it required Mr. Baxter's signature on a number of documents, one of which was a deed to a very small house on Jermyn Street.

Down on the cold street, Mr. Baxter's body moved with the old knowledge. He was slower, but still mighty in his reach, and the one who had come at him with the bottle was soon on the ground. When a second attacker lurched forward, Mr. Baxter split his nose with a light jab. The third man stood snarling, but then backed away when he noticed a figure in the distance running toward them with an enormous pair of scissors.

After the attackers had run off, the man on the ground unfurled like some rare plant. The tailor put down his garment scissors and introduced himself as Colin. Then he pointed in the direction of his shop, and completely out of breath, said: "From New & Lingwood, first floor. Shoes to order, and ready-to-wear."

Mr. Baxter judged him to be about the same age as himself, but with a fuller head of hair and a slight South African accent.

"Charlie Baxter."

"I know who you are," Colin said, breathlessly. "The Menace of Mile End."

Mr. Baxter flushed and tightened the string on his dressing gown.

The man on the ground leaned on his hands and vomited.

"He's the one been making all this noise," Colin said.

Then he looked around at all the clothes. "I suppose we'd better pick these up," he said. "If you give them to me, Mr. Baxter, I'll fold them back into the bag."

After that, Mr. Baxter scooped the boy into his arms and carried him upstairs.

Colin watched in wonder as Mr. Baxter removed pieces of glass from the boy's face with a pair of tweezers. Then he ran hot water in the sink, and opened a bottle of witch hazel. After finding an old roll of bandage in a cupboard, he wrapped his wounds with the gentleness of snow.

The kettle didn't take long to boil.

They all drank tea until the windows glowed.

They also ate honey biscuits from Fortnum & Mason. On the tin, animals played musical instruments.

The young man didn't say much, but accepted each cup of tea with both hands. He also kept checking that his bag of clothes hadn't moved from the hall.

Mr. Baxter thought the boy had a good face. His profile was delicate, with high, almost regal cheekbones that captured light on their descent. And there was something plain and pure about his eyes – something true and uncomplicated; something steady which, under the right circumstances, could be lifted like a jewel from a crevasse. And it probably wouldn't cost the earth for Colin to knock him up a suit and some pajamas, Mr. Baxter thought – give him something to do with that enormous pair of scissors.

Before going to bed himself, it occurred to Mr. Baxter that the man sleeping quietly in his back bedroom might wake up and kill him. But then he was only a boy – just a tired weight in an old man's arms, and there's something sacred about sleep – Mr. Baxter reasoned, nature's way of saving us from ourselves.

And – as he'd pointed out to Colin earlier, the back bedroom was already made up, as though the whole thing had been arranged long ago.

When Mr. Baxter woke in the late afternoon, it was clear that the young man had tried to make the bed before he left.

It wasn't a bad job.

The sheets were pulled up, but not even, and there were creases and dents, as though he had sat back down again.

Mr. Baxter stirred a pot of tea and looked out the window – past the old cheese shop and into New & Lingwood, where several mannequins looked dumbly into street, their limbs divided with lines and numbers.

Mr. Baxter went for his daily walk, as usual, but without his coat. On his way home, he stopped into one of the less expensive men's outfitters on Jermyn Street where he purchased a full-length double-breasted winter coat with brass buttons. When the shopkeeper insisted that Mr. Baxter try it on to prove that it wasn't going to fit over his enormous frame, Mr. Baxter growled at him to mind his own business.

When he got home, he hung the coat on the back of the door. He made a cup of tea, and then drank it very hot, admiring his purchase.

Then all the shops began to close.

Another day was almost over.

Men with briefcases and umbrellas hurried home to their wives and children. The radio said that snow was finally coming, that London would be thick with it by morning. Mr. Baxter imagined it – the hard cold broken into tiny pieces. Brightness falling and filling the corners of an old city. And then for a day or two after – the language of footprints, a Braille of human desire.

After listening to the 6 o' clock news, Mr. Baxter tied on his old apron, and reached into the highest cupboard for a bag of flour. On his way home that day, he had also popped into Wiltons for a couple of fish. The staff were more friendly than usual and wouldn't take a penny.

And at the small, bustling Tesco Metro Supermarket on the corner of Jermyn Street, Mr. Baxter picked out some round Jersey potatoes, a pot of cream, and a bunch of chives.

The good thing about fish pie, he thought – is that it keeps.

But somehow he knew it wouldn't go to waste, and as it bubbled in the blazing oven, and the sky split in a fury of silent falling, Mr. Baxter opened every window in the house. For the great hunger that filled London was no longer his own.

SIMON VAN BOOY GREW UP IN WALES. HE IS THE AUTHOR OF SEVERAL BOOKS, INCLUDING THE FRANK O'CONNOR INTERNATIONAL STORY AWARD-WINNING COLLECTION *LOVE BEGINS IN WINTER*. HE HAS WRITTEN FOR THE *NEW YORK TIMES*, *THE GUARDIAN*, *THE TIMES*, THE BBC, NATIONAL PUBLIC RADIO AND *ELLE MEN* (CHINA), WHERE HE HAS A MONTHLY COLUMN. HIS NEW NOVEL WILL BE PUBLISHED NEXT YEAR.